A WORTHWHILE
ERROR

A WORTHWHILE ERROR

The **History** of **Francis House** **Children's Hospice**

ANDY BUCKLEY

FRANCIS HOUSE
CHILDREN'S HOSPICE

First published in Great Britain by Francis House Family Trust 2023

Francis House Family Trust
390 Parrswood Road
Didsbury
Manchester
M20 5NA

Website www.francishouse.org.uk

ISBN: 978-1-3999-6613-9

Designed, edited and typeset in 11.5 point Minion Pro by Merlin Unwin Books, Ludlow
www.merlinunwin.co.uk

Printed by Akcent Media UK

Whilst every effort has been made in the research and writing of this book, any author errors are unintenional

CONTENTS

*Dedicated to the vision of
Sister Aloysius and Father Tom
and all the families who have passed through
the doors of Francis House.*

FOREWORD BY
SIR WARREN SMITH
KCVO KSTJ JP

The regional television programme *Granada News* reported in 1990 that a new children's hospice was to be built in Didsbury. A few days later, I happened to pass a temporary charity shop on School Lane in aid of the hospice and asked if this was the same charity, as I wanted to donate but needed some reassurance.

Some 24 hours later, Bernard Nagle, the new fundraising manager, came to tell the whole story, and I was hooked. Shortly afterwards, he introduced me to Sister Aloysius and Mgr. Tom Mulheran. Sister Aloysius was a formidable and direct-speaking individual who didn't take prisoners. It was evident that she had an unstoppable vision.

Father Tom's warm and wonderful smile welcomed so many of us to Francis House. Behind that friendly avuncular façade was an inspired intellect who understood the vision and how the dream would be fulfilled. There is absolutely no doubt that without these two individuals, and the generous support of the Sisters, this project would never have got off the ground.

Sir Warren Smith KCVO KSTJ JP

Word soon went around about this much-needed project as supporters spread the news. I remember meeting a group of ladies at home who were the driving force behind the first Francis House Ball. In addition, some very generous donors appeared. There was such enthusiasm and support that things seemed to move forward quickly.

In 1991, I was one of the lucky ones to be presented to Diana, Princess of Wales, when she came to open the hospice. Some 25 years later, as Lord-Lieutenant, I had the honour of escorting the Duke and Duchess of Cornwall around Francis House. It was poignant for several of us who had attended the opening and were here to celebrate the 25th anniversary.

As the hospice approaches its 32nd birthday, there is an opportunity to reflect on the people and personalities who have ensured its success. Two individuals come to mind. Kirsty Howard, born in 1995, was first admitted to Francis House in 1999 and Susie Mathis, presenter and broadcaster and a passionate supporter. This remarkable partnership came together in our hour of need in 1999 and led a fundraising campaign that raised over £5m.

Later, I shared a platform with Sir Alex Ferguson and Kirsty as we launched another £2m appeal in Manchester Town Hall. She had a wonderful, warm personality and was always smiling. When I talked to her, it was apparent how fulfilling she found being able to make a significant contribution to the future of Francis House. She received many tributes for her work and inspiration, culminating in the Diana Award.

We have many unsung heroes who raise money throughout the year for Francis House. Donations come from golf days, coffee mornings, balls, donations, legacies, sponsored climbs, walks, runs, a Christmas carol service and our Easter chicks who made the television news. Our friends and supporters cannot be thanked enough. They have brought us through the last 30-odd years and will be the key to the future. To me, they are all heroes.

Without the support of so many members of the Francis House Family, we would not exist. But unfortunately, the government provides only a modest proportion of the costs: less than 20 per cent. The rest of the money comes from the generosity and activities of our supporters – people like you and me, the readers of this book.

Many ask why the government doesn't do more. I haven't got the answer. But I know that Francis House allows us to share the responsibility of supporting these young people and their families. To show today that we care and are in this together; they are not alone.

During the first few years of opening, the youngest son of a friend, a teenager, had some challenging problems and the expectation of a short life. Nevertheless, he taught me a lot about the ethos of Francis House. His parents booked him in for a short stay, and it soon became clear how much he enjoyed his visit because after that he would book himself in from time to time. The penny dropped for me. This was not a place for people to die but quite the opposite, where people live and enjoy life. It gave him, for the first time, a real opportunity to have control over what he wanted to do. He could put himself in a place where he was safe and had friends and a new level of independence. At the same time, his parents and family knew that he was safe and happy, surrounded by love and care.

He was an outstanding young man with a great passion and knowledge of classical music; he went to the Hallé and visited Salzburg with his parents to see Mozart's birthplace; he had such a joy for life and to see the help he got from Francis House both humbled and inspired me to support this wonderful organisation for over 30 years.

During that time, Francis House has been governed by a Board of Trustees, who have given their time, energy, and support. They have needed courage as the organisation has expanded, the overheads have continued to grow and so has their liability. Changing legislation has often increased their responsibility. Yet they have never wavered in their support. They are unpaid but contribute enormous value to Francis House; for that they must be thanked by all who come through its doors.

The big heroes are those who work at Francis House, the team led and inspired by Revd David Ireland. David has been a trustee, architect and chief executive and has been the guiding light throughout the history of this organisation. He has been supported by an incredible team of people: the carers, administrators, fundraisers, those who maintain the building and wonderful garden and volunteers who are exceptionally generous with their time.

Francis House is an inspirational team effort. The strength of this passionate team showed itself during the pandemic when it was the only children's hospice between Loughborough and the Scottish border that stayed open during lockdown. A remarkable achievement. The contribution made by David and his team and the hospice's success has been recognised by visitors from as far away as Japan, Eastern Europe and throughout the United Kingdom, all discovering the secret of Francis House. It is a world-class organisation.

Francis House now operates from three sites, offering different provisions in south Manchester. It is driven by need and continues to grow as it supports new challenges. We rely heavily on the goodwill of our supporters and friends, without whom we could not continue, and we always will. As I mentioned earlier, that support is not only financial. It demonstrates that we care and are part of a broader family that wants to do something to share and show the families who come here that they are not alone.

It has been a privilege to write the foreword to this extraordinary book and congratulate the author, Andy Buckley, on a real 'tour de force'. He has devoted much time to interviewing people and researching so much that has not been written down, the many anecdotes that have captured Francis House's spirit.

It has allowed me to reflect on over 30 years that have flown by. To reminisce about Sister Aloysius, the Sisters, Father Tom and the people and families I have known who have stayed at Francis House. To appreciate what Francis House has achieved. It is a remarkable organisation, better expressed as a large family. We can all feel part of it and support it. But, to those like me whose enthusiasm is not matched by their energy, perhaps the time has come to think about a legacy.

INTRODUCTION

'I knew my little boy was never going to grow up. My very own Peter Pan. When we were introduced to Francis House it was like a fairy godmother had waved a magic wand and everything started to seem a little easier than I'd first imagined.'

A young mother describes exactly what Francis House Children's Hospice means to her. Just one of many touching stories about one of Manchester's best-loved charities. Her experience is replicated by countless other parents for whom Francis House has been a lifeline. It is hard now to imagine a world without it.

For more than three decades the hospice has been a haven for children, young people, and their families. Each with their own unique story. Many facing unbearable everyday challenges others would probably find hard to comprehend. Families are relieved to find respite through the doors of Francis House, which enjoys a secluded

Francis House Children's Hospice in Didsbury

location on Parrswood Road, Didsbury, in the leafy suburbs south of Manchester.

A centre of excellence providing respite care for youngsters with life-limiting and life-threatening conditions. A role it proudly shares with 41 other children's hospices across the United Kingdom. Yet Francis House might not be here without the vision and passion of a religious Sister whose steadfast belief turned a dream into reality. The leadership and conviction of Sister Aloysius transformed the lives of families from across the north-west and beyond.

An amazing woman whose Catholic faith took her and her loyal helpers on a remarkable journey, leaving a powerful legacy. There is no charge to stay at Francis House. The vast majority of running costs come from the generosity of people who have never even met the children and families they are helping.

The hospice is a place of fun where precious memories are created. Where lives are fulfilled, rather than merely waiting for them to end. Where a child, or young adult, coping with disability or illness achieves their dream. To others this might appear a fairly routine task. But for the special visitors to Francis House it represents a joyous triumph. Children under 16 years of age with a life-limiting or life-threatening condition can be referred to Francis House. Unlike some other hospices, there is no upper age limit. So once accepted, young adults in their twenties, or even thirties, continue to receive care.

The Francis House story is quite extraordinary. The project went from drawing board to a high-profile royal opening by Princess Diana in record time. The history of the hospice probably divides neatly into two halves.

The first stage saw a period of consolidation as staff and volunteers gradually built upon the initial success of actually getting the hospice up and running and being able to afford to pay for it. Financial backing presented a major challenge in itself and without a generous loan from Salford R.C. Diocese the project would never have got off the ground.

The second stage, from around 2011, is a story of expansion. This development was only possible due to the hard work and commitment from the early pioneers whose dedication and unwavering belief created the facility. The hospice doubled in size in 2014 when Francis Lodge opened as a parent-free zone, providing respite care for those over 16 years of age. A residential facility at 463 Parrswood Road and later 92 Barcicroft Road were also opened to cater for a growing need. New medical interventions and improved care methods mean that severely disabled youngsters are now living longer. That, in turn, means more respite help is needed.

Francis House is a friendly home from home, supporting approximately 2,000 people at any one time. The care is diverse and includes respite, homecare, sibling support, end-of-life care, emotional and bereavement support. Legal advice and chiropractic care are also offered.

For the record, 91.78p in every pound donated goes directly towards care, far more than most other charities. Francis House needs £4.7m each year to stay open. It is not part of any statutory health provision. The care is additional to that provided by the National Health Service.

The number of families on the Francis House roll stands at 573 in 2023. In 2005, the total was 138. That huge rise shows both the charity's progress and development and the ever-increasing demand for its valued services.

The hospice received 17 per cent of running costs from public money in 2022. The percentage was slightly higher due to a Covid grant of £150,000. Annual revenue from public funds has always varied and hovered around 15 per cent or just under, until the pandemic in 2020. There was no government help in the early days when Francis House had to generate all its own income. When State help was eventually forthcoming, the percentage was tiny and had grown to only four per cent of running costs by 2005.

Francis House also helps families outside the United Kingdom. It has extended the arm of friendship far and wide to countries such as Bosnia, Belarus, Japan, USA, Czech Republic, Canada and Australia. Like-minded organisations overseas have been assisted in their efforts to establish much-needed respite care for children with life-limiting or life-threatening illnesses. Francis House has a fascinating and compelling heritage. It has been around for almost a third of a century. Here is the story so far ...

The outdoor play area at Francis House

CHAPTER 1

HOW IT ALL STARTED

Turn the clock back to the late 1980s and it was easy to understand why there was a need for more children's hospices. There were only four in the country – in Oxford, Wetherby, Birmingham and Cambridge. A geographical spread that presented a nightmare for parents of sick children from Greater Manchester and beyond.

Helen House in Oxford – the first children's hospice in the world – had opened in November 1982. The next to welcome families was Martin House in the Yorkshire market town of Wetherby in 1987. By the time plans were being made for Francis House, two other facilities in the West Midlands and Cambridgeshire had also opened their doors.

Demand to use these hospices was great. It soon became clear that more were urgently needed to serve other parts of the country. The overwhelming demand for places meant families – many from the north-west – were reluctantly being turned away. For those able to secure a place it meant a trek to the other side of the Pennines to Martin House.

Staff there were overstretched and relieved to learn that help would soon be forthcoming. At the start of the nineties, Manchester was

coming to the rescue with its own hospice, located in Didsbury.

The proposed catchment area would extend beyond Greater Manchester into North Wales, North Cheshire and South Lancashire. It would make history as the first children's hospice to be initiated by the Catholic Church, catering for children and families of all faiths and none.

The Catholic Children's Rescue Society, within the Diocese of Salford, had identified an alarming lack of respite provision for children with a short life expectancy. The Society's origins went back more than a century to 1886. The voluntary organisation was founded by Herbert Vaughan, the then Bishop of Salford. His aim was to provide for children baptised into the Catholic Church who, for one reason or another, were deprived of family life and whose faith had been endangered.

A model of the future ... Monsignor Thomas Mulheran (second right) shows The Lord Mayor of Manchester Cllr John Gilmore and Mayoress Mavis Gilmore a vision of Francis House with the Rt. Rev. Patrick Kelly far left and Robin Wood CBE far right

Bishop Vaughan sought the help of Alice Ingram, a milliner from Rochdale who, in 1883, had founded the Congregation of Franciscan Missionaries of St Joseph. Alice, by then known as Mother Francis, provided Sisters to care for these children in need. So began a long successful relationship between the Catholic Children's Rescue Society of Salford and the Sisters of the Franciscan Missionaries of St Joseph, known as the Rescue Sisters. More than a century later that partnership would result in the opening of Francis House on Friday, 1 November 1991.

The Rescue Society cared for children deprived of home life in a number of residential homes in Manchester and surrounding areas. Adoption and fostering were at the heart of the Society's family placement work. Some children had severe disabilities and there was a realisation that additional support services were required for them. The Society was used to adapting to changing times.

For instance, it had been forced to reassess its childcare provision following the 1948 Children Act. The legislation made local authorities responsible for the care of any child whose parents were unable to look after them, assuming it was in the child's best interests. Local authorities would only place children with independent voluntary organisations, such as the Rescue Society, if they conformed to these new government guidelines.

The Society knew it had to meet these new demands to continue caring for children who needed help. The post-war years were therefore a period of development and change for the Franciscan Missionaries of St Joseph and the Rescue Society.

The war years had meant that only essential repair work had been carried out at homes due to shortages of material and labour. Initially, fewer children went into Society homes until these larger homes were remodelled and converted into more modern smaller units. Once that investment and transition was made, buildings were inspected, approved and registered by the Home Office and that led to a significant increase in the number of children admitted.

The general feeling was that large group homes shielded children from the realities of life, while smaller family units were a more suitable substitute for a child's own home. This willingness to make change further strengthened the bond between the Sisters and the Rescue Society.

A driving force behind ensuring a more intimate family environment for children was Monsignor Gerard McCormack, who served as secretary of the Rescue Society from 1955 until 1977 when ill health forced him to stand down. He was replaced by his assistant, Monsignor Thomas Mulheran, who had joined in 1971. The family placement work highlighted an issue addressed in a book

celebrating the Rescue Society's centenary in 1986. Tellingly, an excerpt read:

'As the number of disabled children placed in adoptive and foster homes increased, so did the awareness of the pressures which were being placed on these families with never a break by day and frequently not even at night. Accordingly, a respite service was set up by which these children could be admitted to a children's home for the occasional weekend and for parts of holiday time, if necessary other times too.

'In this way, parents have a little break to recoup their energy and give time to one another and other children in the family. The service is not exclusively for adopted or foster children. It was offered to families referred to the Society. The children are well received by other youngsters in the home, from whom it seems to bring out the best and the children seem to adapt quickly to their surroundings.'

The Mount Carmel home, run by Sister Nicola Haarhuis and lay staff, was modified to allow for the care of disabled young people. It was located at 463, Parrswood Road, Didsbury, an address that would become synonymous with Francis House in the fullness of time. Back in the late 80s, as Rescue Society premises, it provided much-needed respite facilities for disabled children.

It was soon apparent, though, that something more was required. Something far more substantial. More provision was needed. The demand from families had shown that. A young girl, Teeraj Daas, sadly passed away in April 1991 while staying at Mount Carmel. Poignantly, she was given zero as her number on the register since Francis House was not open by then. Teeraj, who was under the care of Sister Nicola and her team, never lived to see Francis House but she was looked after using the Francis House philosophy.

Mount Carmel was not the solution, despite the best intentions. Significantly, though, it had provided a vital clue which was to shape the future. The facility – two semi-detached houses knocked into one – had exposed a severe lack of provision for families of children with a short life expectancy in the north-west. The issue was discussed initially by three senior figures in the Rescue Society – secretary Father Thomas Mulheran, Sister Aloysius and Jim Buggy.

Sister Aloysius founded the Rescue Society's fostering department, managing the service for many years. Jim Buggy was also an expert in childcare. As a senior social worker, his background included developing care for disabled children within Manchester's social services department. The trio agreed there was an urgent need for a hospice for severely disabled children in the north-west.

The archives at Francis House Children's Hospice provide a fascinating insight into

Sister Aloysius with fellow members of the Rescue Council in 1986

the challenges faced by parents of children with life-limiting illnesses at the end of the 1980s.

One document reads:

'Any respite which a family may require can only be obtained by the child returning to hospital and when life expectancy is short and hospital philosophy is about cure, families resist this and consequently become more and more burdened.'

Children with life-limiting illnesses and their families had many unmet needs. These included:

● A sense of isolation.
● The inability of hospitals to provide for families, especially where there were brothers and sisters.
● A lack of any form of ongoing support, except for children suffering cancerous illnesses.

The Rescue Council – effectively the board of the Catholic Children's Rescue Society – appointed a sub-committee in January 1990. Its brief was to research and report on the need for hospice facilities for children in the north-west. Members included Sister Aloysius, Jim Buggy, State Registered Nurse Louise Burke, Paddy Clifford, John Cox, Bernard Lofthouse and Sister Austin, who was co-opted as acting secretary.

The group quickly set about their task. They spoke to parents, paediatric specialists and health authorities to determine what provision was available for children with terminal illnesses. Fact-finding visits were also made to Helen House, and Martin House, the only hospice available to families living north of Birmingham all the way up to Scotland.

Close links were established with the nearest hospice, Martin House, which provided invaluable practical assistance. Its Administrator Robin Wood and Senior Nurse Lenore Hill emphasised the urgent need for a hospice on the other side of the Pennines. Sister Aloysius held a meeting of the Sisters at Our Lady of Lourdes Convent, situated on Parrswood Road in Didsbury, on Thursday, 1 February 1990.

She suggested the Sisters vacate the Convent so it could be converted into a children's hospice. It was a seminal moment in the history of Francis House.

The Sisters readily agreed to the idea which would see them re-housed in different communities where they could continue their ministries. At this stage the project was kept under wraps and it would not become general knowledge until Rescue staff were informed.

Jim Buggy clarified an important difference between Mount Carmel and the hospice project at the first meeting of the newly formed Rescue Council sub-committee on Thursday, 8 February 1990.

He said: 'Mount Carmel provides respite care for mentally and physically handicapped children, but not children with short life-expectancy. The proposed facility will be for children with life-threatening illnesses, for which there are no known cures at present and for whom life expectancy is limited.'

1ST MEETING OF RESCUE COUNCIL SUB-COMMITTEE ON THE
OUR LADY OF LOURDES CENTRE PROJECT

Held at "Maryhill", Burnley, on Thursday, 8th February, 1990

PRESENT:- Sister Aloysius, FMSJ - Rescue Council Member
          Mrs. L. Burke   - Rescue Council Member
          Mr. J. Cox   - Rescue Council Member
          Mr. P. Clifford   - Rescue Council Member
          Mr. J. Buggy   - Senior Social Worker -
                                 Spec. Projects with
                                 Rescue Society
          Sister Austin, FMSJ - Co-opted, acting
                                 secretary.

02-01-90 Sister Aloysius informed those present that research,
          into the need for respite care facilities for children
          with terminal illnesses, and the feasibility of basing
          such a project at Our Lady of Lourdes Convent, Didsbury,
          has so far been "under wraps". As it will soon be
          necessary for architects and others to study the
          present building with a view to change of usage, Sister
          has now spoken to the Sisters of the Community, who
          gave a very positive reception to the idea. Until the
          Rescue Staff are told of the project, it will not
          become general knowledge.

03-01-90 Sr. Aloysius said that the first task of this sub-
          committee is to establish a Trust Fund and in order
          to do this the aims and objectives of the project
          need to be clarified and spelt out.

04-01-90 Jim Buggy clarified the difference between "Mount
          Carmel", recently opened by Rescue, and this project.
          "Mount Carmel" provides respite care for mentally and
          physically handicapped children, but not children with
          a short life-expectancy.

          Our Lady of Lourdes Centre will be for children with
          life-threatening illnesses, for which there are no
          known cures at present and for whom the life-expectancy
          is limited.

05-01-90 The Aims and Objectives were discussed and resulted in
          the following:-

          a) to care for children, of any faith or race, with a
             life-threatening illness;

          b) to provide fullness of quality of life and comfort
             for the limited life-span;

          c) to allow children to die with dignity;

/Continued...

The minutes of the first meeting of the Rescue Council sub-committee

was a much-needed centre. A children's hospice in the north-west was not a new idea. Plans were already being drawn up to create a facility in Chorley, some 30 miles from Manchester.

Fundraising efforts in the Lancashire town had only achieved limited success until that point. Father Mulheran and Sister Aloysius met organisers from that other project to exchange ideas and glean information. The two groups agreed to collaborate, but without a formal partnership.

A fundamental question centred on whether it was necessary to have two children's hospices in the north-west and whether both would be sustainable? The decision was made that there WAS enough scope to accommodate both Francis House and a site in Chorley, to be known as Derian House.

Derian House – strategically located just a couple of miles from the M61 motorway – eventually opened in October 1993. Francis House would assist Derian House through the process, sharing information about its own experiences. But back in early 1990, plans for Francis House were gaining momentum as detailed research was undertaken.

It was thought there were at least 250 children in the north-west with short life expectancy who would use a hospice, though another estimate put the figure closer to 400. Whatever the actual total, it was clear this

Meetings took place with parents, teachers, social workers and other parties with a vested interest in the care of children with disabilities. The parental view was pretty obvious. They felt there was a huge need, an opinion shared by many others.

There was, however, opposition to the idea. Some senior health care experts were concerned that if money went into a children's hospice it might take resources away from paediatric units in the area. That school of thought was not shared by paediatric consultant Michael Burke, based at Withington Hospital. Michael (husband of Louise, who was on the Rescue Society Council of Management and a nurse) was a keen advocate of a new hospice and threw his support behind the plan.

The only respite on offer for parents was hospital, but this took the child away from them. Their dream was a hospice, dedicated to the care of the child, with accommodation for family members when required. A recurring theme among feedback from parents was the desperate need for a break in the 24-hour care cycle of a child. An all too familiar response was that the only time they experienced respite came when a child was in hospital.

But that arrangement did not suit parents who felt guilty about letting their loved ones stay on an acute ward. Nor did it help the child for whom hospital usually meant painful, or invasive treatments. Equally, it did not suit the hospital where the emphasis was on treatment and cure.

The next step was to create the hospice. The hard work was only just beginning.

With the need evident, the big concern was funding. How to afford to change a convent into a hospice and then run it? This presented a dilemma – whether to delay any action until funds were raised, or to make a start and have faith that there would be sufficient resources? Sadly, children of families already known to the Rescue Society, who needed the support of a hospice, would probably not live long enough if they had to wait up to four years for funds to be raised.

Salford R.C. Diocese supported the decision to start as soon as possible. The Bishop of Salford made an initial loan of £750,000 to enable work on the new hospice to go ahead. The bill for the project was £900,000. This included £270,000 to adapt the convent and £240,000 for a new extension. Special items, external work, VAT and fees accounted for the £900,000 estimate.

> By March 1990, a total of £54,000 had been made in donations. A decent start considering the hospice proposal had only just become public knowledge. Inevitably, costs increased particularly as the first contractor went into liquidation. A further £100,000 loan from the diocese was needed in February 1993. In making the loans, the diocese emphasised the importance of Francis House, which is pro-life, believing that every life is a gift and is owed respect, love and nurturing care.

Meanwhile, during the planning stage families were having to make a 90-minute journey across the M62 for respite care at

Martin House. It was estimated that around 50 families were travelling from Manchester to Wetherby for this purpose. For others, though, no such option was available. There was nowhere for them to go.

At that point Martin House were having to limit the geographical boundaries for referrals. The north was desperate for another children's hospice, and the need was now!

On Thursday, 8 March 1990, the Rescue Council made the formal decision to go ahead with plans for a children's hospice, having considered the monthly reports of the sub-committee. The Bishop of Salford, The Right Reverend Patrick Kelly, was chair of the Rescue Council.

He insisted the hospice should be a separate enterprise, reinforcing the principle that it was part of the diocese's pro-life stance.

Aims and objectives were outlined as follows:
- Care for children of any race, or faith, with a life-threatening illness.
- Provide full quality of life and comfort within the child's limitations.
- Allow children to die with dignity.
- Support the children's families, emotionally, physically and spiritually.
- Provide an outreach service to children and families.
- Allow families the choice of their children being cared for at home, or in the hospice where parents and other family members can be supported by caring staff.
- Allow the pace to be at that of the child and family, and not subject to the necessary routine of a hospital.

It was pointed out that the hospice required a new way of thinking. Until this point the work of the Rescue Society had been promoting life whereas this facility, while promoting the highest quality of life, must prepare children, their parents and family members for death.

With no public funds available, setting up a hospice was a step taken in great faith.

The aims and objectives of the trust/limited company were to manage and develop the project and raise funds.

The catchment area was the Diocese of Salford and surrounding areas in the north-west. Architect David Ireland, of Messrs Hulme Upright & Partners, was commissioned to draw up plans to adapt the building. Royal support was also secured. The Duchess of Norfolk, joint chair and founder of Help the Hospices, agreed to become a patron. Such high-profile backing added further credibility to the ambitious venture.

Meanwhile, Derian House fundraiser Margaret Vinten was approached for advice. She had set up three successful nursing homes so knew how to bring projects to life. All kinds of fundraising avenues were explored, including a request for help from the BBC Children in Need Appeal. The net was spread far and wide to finance a project that was entirely self-supporting.

With such a considerable amount needed, it was suggested that a full-time professional fundraiser should be employed. An appointment was duly made in the summer of 1991. Importantly, it was recognised that there should be no encroachment on areas and personnel already supporting the Rescue Society.

The convent of our Lady of Lourdes home to the FMSJ Sisters

Suggestions on staffing were made by Sister Aloysius. Roles included an administrator, head nurse, cook, 16 care staff comprising State Registered Nurses and other qualified personnel, a social worker, waking night nurses and volunteers. The Sisters living in the convent were informed of the Rescue Council's decision to proceed with the hospice and they were asked to pray for God's blessing on the undertaking. The Sisters would be relocated into three local houses belonging to the Rescue Society. The following weeks saw a flurry of activity.

A visit was made to St Ann's Hospice in Heald Green, Stockport. The charity, which opened in 1971, was one of the oldest adult hospices in the country. Meetings were held with the sub-committee, Architect and the Bank of Ireland about setting up an account.

Planning permission was sought from Manchester City Council on Friday, 4 May 1990 and granted on Tuesday, 28 August.

A Memorandum of Association was drawn up by solicitors Cobbett, Leak, Almond and an Application for Registration as a charity was forwarded to the Charities Commission. Charity status was duly granted on Thursday, 5 July, though this was done by practically sitting on the doorstep of the Charities Commission until registration was given as no serious efforts at fundraising could take place without it.

The Charity Number given was No. 328659. On the same date, The Certificate of Incorporation of a Private Limited Company was also granted - No. 2519173. The limited company option provided more flexibility for the trust, according to legal advice. The charity

Sisters at prayer in the Didsbury chapel in 1981

was to be called the Rainbow Family Trust. The rainbow was considered an appropriate symbol of hope and suited to children.

As the concern was for care of the *total* family, the Rainbow Family Trust was therefore an appropriate title.

The Rainbow Family Trust set up a board of directors. Members were Rt. Rev. Patrick A Kelly, Bishop of Salford; Sister Aloysius, Chairperson; Fr. Thomas Mulheran; Fr. Paul Mitcheson; Dr Michael Burke; John Cox; Bernard Lofthouse and Paddy Clifford. They were also members of a Council of Management which included Ged Cosgrove, accountant; Patricia Sturrock, solicitor; Dr Hugh Fay, retired GP; Martin Lochery, headteacher, St John Vianney School; Louise Burke SRN. Three other sub-committees for finance, administration and services were also established.

Parents of children who would use the hospice were told of the plans, along with local residents. The neighbours fully accepted there would be disruption and inconvenience during the building period. Ministers from local churches were also asked to support the project. Events were moving at pace. Meetings were held with the clergy of the Diocese of Salford, partly to explain that the Rainbow Family Trust was an entirely separate charity to the Rescue Society which had inspired its emergence.

It was emphasised that while Rainbow would seek funding from across the entire region, it did not want to intrude on traditional support among parishes for the Rescue Society. If a parish requested a speaker, Rainbow would happily provide one, but the trust would not make any approaches themselves.

Sister Aloysius expressed the need for a more firmly structured management committee, proposing Bishop Kelly act as chair of trustees instead of her. As secretary to the trust, she felt holding both roles was inappropriate. On Friday, 29 November the building contract was signed by Sister Aloysius in the presence of Father Mulheran and David Ireland. A momentous landmark for the newly created charity.

Monday, 10 December 1990 was a poignant and emotional day. The Sisters moved out of the Convent as the builders moved in – quite literally. Leaving their happy home for 30 years, the 16 remaining Sisters were dispersed to other accommodation owned by the Rescue Society. They moved into smaller houses around the city where they could offer new ministries to local communities.

David Ireland, who would later become Chief Executive Officer of Francis House, recalled:

'I'll never forget the sight of the Sisters' possessions being wheeled down the drive as the builders moved in to transform what was their home into a place for families to rest and recuperate on their difficult journeys.

'Francis House was born out of their sacrificial gift. Thank you to all of the Sisters past and present for the major part you've played in the care of children and families over the last century here in Didsbury.'

The convent which became Francis House Children's Hospice

No sooner had the Sisters' bags been packed and taken down the convent driveway, than the traditional turf-cutting ceremony was performed at 3pm that same afternoon. Bishop Kelly said the hospice should be called Francis House in memory of the sacrifice made by the Franciscan Sisters.

Unfortunately, the building construction company Donnelly Construction Ltd was placed in the hands of receivers in late January 1991. Previous tenders were considered, and Eric Wright Construction was appointed with work resuming in mid February. Thankfully, hardly any building time was lost due to bad weather, even during the depths of winter.

Margaret Hickie

In the spring of 1991, the Society received a letter from the Vatican, conveying the good wishes of Pope John Paul II.

On Saturday, 1 June 1991, Margaret Hickie was appointed Head of Care. Competition for the post was strong with 40 applicants for this pioneering nursing position. Her priority was to identify children and families, meet them all and finalise interview dates for her staff. As numbers of children were expected to build up slowly and with money in short supply, staggered start dates were agreed for subsequent care appointments.

Some 15 staff started work on Monday, 21 October with a week-long orientation period, while a further seven staff began their roles at the start of 1992. As word of the proposed hospice spread, schools, pubs, rotary clubs and all kinds of groups began to support the endeavour. Donations flooded in. The money was urgently needed. The original budget for the hospice was £1m, though the estimate for capital costs, including furniture and medical equipment, later rose to £1.5m.

The £750,000 loan from the Bishop of Salford had eased the financial pressure initially. By the time an additional £100,000 was loaned some 16 months after opening, daily running costs had risen to around £3,000. Fundraising was also a factor. Thankfully, donations had almost reached £1m around the time of opening. Awareness among the public was high but sustaining that level of profile and support was another challenge.

Alas, no government help was forthcoming, while local authority grants were negligible.

A wall hanging in the chapel depicting Creation

Other key appointments during the build-up to the opening saw Bernard Nagle appointed Fundraiser in July 1991 after Shaunagh Ward took over as Administrative Secretary. Bernard was formerly an employee of the Catholic Children's Rescue Society. Part of premises at St John Vianney School in Stretford were subsequently used as a fundraising office.

A meeting was held with ministers of various local churches at the end of October 1991 to inform them about the hospice and invite their support and involvement at a later stage. Father Earley, of St. Ambrose Church, Chorlton, and Reverend Taylor, of Grosvenor St. Aidan's in Didsbury, would later visit to pledge their support. Local GP, Dr Stanley Goodman, offered the services of his Ladybarn practice. It was the start of a successful partnership which continued until June 1995 when the demands of Francis House had become too great for the busy surgery.

Lynn Brammer, a young mother who lived locally, was commissioned to design two wall hangings for the chapel – one depicting Creation and the other, Fruits of the Earth. These creative and original works would be greatly admired through the years, not least by the many embroidery and other artistic groups visiting on viewing days.

The building was handed over in the first week of October, three weeks after the due date and only three weeks before the arrival of the first families. The only incomplete parts were the chapel, mortuary and hydrotherapy pool. The conversion work was recognised with an award sometime later in the 'design in a care setting' category.

An open week took place in mid October, with each day dedicated to a particular group of friends and fundraisers. Visitors eager to catch a glimpse of the new hospice included the Sisters who had given up their home and

Rescue staff who had watched the changes with great interest from the windows of their Society offices situated in the same grounds. Other guests were newly appointed Rainbow staff, local mayors, neighbours, fundraisers, media, priests and ministers.

Robin Wood and Lenore Hill, from Martin House, were also given a warm welcome. They had become good friends by now and their assistance had been invaluable. Another visitor was Charles Morris, the former MP for Openshaw, who had helped to secure a high-profile royal opening. Indeed, it was during the open week that confirmation was received that Her Royal Highness the Princess of Wales would officially open Francis House on Monday, 25 November 1991. The Diana visit was also a tribute to the planning undertaken by dedicated supporter Moira Rossiter.

Charles Morris's brother Alf was also a politician. Alf was MP for Wythenshawe and a champion of the rights of the disabled. He was the first Minister for the Disabled globally. In 1970, he introduced the Chronically Sick and Disabled Persons Act, the first in the world to recognise and give rights to people with disabilities. It was hard to believe that the welfare of the disabled had been ignored until then. Alf also accepted an offer to become a patron of Francis House, a fitting appointment in view of his parliamentary campaign.

With so many visitors and new carpets everywhere, staff breathed a sigh of relief when the weather remained fine throughout the open week. An orientation period for the first wave of staff then took place. Margaret Hickie's team included registered children's nurses, nursery nurses, a teacher

The lounge at Francis House as it looks today

and physiotherapist, together with chef Dean Jenkins, maintenance manager Joe McQuillan and house manager Sister Austin. All were under the direction of Sister Aloysius, Administrator and Company Secretary.

Most of the staff were coming to Francis House straight from NHS hospitals so the philosophy and work practice would be completely different. They had to adapt to a new culture with the emphasis on working in close partnership with parents who were the experts in caring for their own children. Quality of life and care was the approach, rather than cure and discharge. They also had to cope with whole families and not just the sick child. Added to that, they were new to the job just like everyone else. Their courage facing up to the enormity of the task in this pioneering work had to be admired.

The first families were booked to arrive on Friday, 1 November 1991, more than three weeks before the official opening. However, a family emergency meant the doors were actually opened the previous Monday, 28 October. A senior paediatric oncology nurse at The Christie telephoned to ask if the hospice could take a family immediately.

Their daughter Alanna was at the terminal stage of her illness. Her mother had two other children and was facing a crisis. Her washing line had snapped! Francis House immediately swung into action. By the time the family arrived, with Alanna in an ambulance and her medication checked, the washing and ironing

had been done by enthusiastic hospice staff. Sadly, Alanna passed away. But the raison d'être for Francis House had already become clear. A family with the weight of the world on their shoulders had received practical assistance and loving care in their hour of need.

Dying children and hospitals

Children dying on paediatric hospital wards was a common occurrence in the 1960s and 1970s. Patients of all ages remained in hospital beds for long periods, such was the nature of hospital care. It was not unusual to see children with terminal conditions remain on the same ward for months next to patients convalescing.

Any support and care in the community was almost exclusively geared towards children with oncology related conditions. As the pressure on hospital services increased, there was a change of approach on the wards. The emphasis was on a faster turnover of acute admissions, rather than recuperation and convalescence, thereby reducing the volume of long-term patients.

By the late 1970s and 80s, neither the parents nor the health authorities saw an acute children's ward as the place to come to terms with long-term serious illness. Families experienced neglect of medical and nursing support once their child was discharged from hospital.

In 1976 the Department of Health produced a document called 'Report on Child Health Services – Fit for the Future' which

The stained glass window of the Francis House chapel.

acknowledged the need to provide a 'more child and family-centred service.' Crucially, though, the government lacked the ability to fund more holistic support services due to the ongoing pressure to treat and cure.

That, in turn, led to the development of new palliative care services emerging outside the Health Service in the form of adult and children's hospices. Britain appointed its first paediatric palliative care consultant in the eighties and the children's hospice movement would grow in the following decade to become an essential part of the healthcare spectrum. Hospices, though, were largely self-funded, especially for children. It is an issue which is still controversial to this day.

The Rainbow Dilemma

Francis House is a famous name with a proud tradition for helping children, young adults and their families. But did you know the hospice might have had a completely different name? Rainbow House was under serious consideration as a possible title. The organisation had already set up its charitable status as the Rainbow Family Trust.

But using the Rainbow title within the name of the actual hospice was a non-starter, as there was already a similar charity by the same name. The discovery was made at a medical conference at Regent's College, London, on Monday, 1 October 1990. Sister Aloysius, Sister Austin and State registered nurse Louise Burke were attending the first meeting of the Association for Children with Terminal illnesses.

They learned of the existence of the Rainbow Trust, a separate charity engaged in domiciliary care of children with life-threatening illnesses in their own homes. This organisation requested that the new hospice in Manchester would not be called Rainbow House since they wanted to use that name for their holiday house once established.

In fact, Rainbow had been at the top of a list of possible names under review by Sister Aloysius and her team. So, a change of heart saw Francis House born… and the rest is history.

Above left, the original logo (designed by Sister Austin's brother) changed to the current logo in 2019 to be more inclusive

A picture that tells a thousand words… a rainbow over Francis House

The name Rainbow Family Trust was chosen to convey a name with meaning to people with or without a faith. For those with a faith, a rainbow is a sign of hope; a reminder that God keeps his promises and a symbol of the Resurrection.

For those without a faith, the rainbow is something beautiful and gives joy to the heart even though it does not last long. It also appears when rain and sun struggle in stormy skies. Family is central to the name because the whole family is fundamental to the charity's work.

Francis House honours the sacrifice made by the Congregation of the Franciscan Missionaries of Saint Joseph. Furthermore, Francis of Assisi is a saint acceptable to all people – Christian and non-Christian. His deep compassion and total acceptance of everyone, especially the most vulnerable, is the model and example of the care team at Francis House.

CHAPTER 2

ROYAL VISITS

An air of excitement and anticipation hung over Didsbury and, in particular, Francis House as the day of the royal visit dawned. Diana, Princess of Wales – the most famous woman in the world – was officially opening the new children's hospice. The final frantic preparations had been completed.

Monday, 25 November 1991

The last pictures had been hung, carpets vacuumed to within an inch of their lives, each cloakroom sparkled 'just in case' and numerous cups of coffee were consumed as the final countdown was reached. The day was cold and windy and by 8am the police had been round yet again with the sniffer dogs.

Street barriers were in place and crowds gathered. Children with flowers, old, young, and infirm, all waited eagerly to catch a glimpse of the royal visitor. Families not already in residence arrived by 9am with excited children, scrubbed, shining and dressed for the occasion.

Diana had said she wished to spend her time at Francis House with them. One family present had already suffered the loss of their little girl when Francis House had opened its doors. Official guests arrived and were directed to their designated areas until it seemed Francis House could hold no more.

Every available corner was crammed with friends and benefactors. People who had belief in the project and had supported it generously with their time and money. Among those waiting were Sir Matt Busby, the legendary Manchester United manager, clergy of every denomination, business leaders and volunteers whose heroic work raising funds had made the hospice possible.

Tension mounted as the moment drew near. The royal car finally arrived and amid cheers from the crowds Princess Diana stepped out. The Lord Lieutenant Sir John Timmins greeted her, along with the Lord Mayor of Manchester, Cllr John Gilmore; Bishop Patrick Kelly, from Salford R.C. Diocese; Withington MP Keith Bradley; Administrator Sister Aloysius and Head of Care Margaret Hickie.

Neighbours hung over the wall and Rescue Society office workers peered out of windows and lined the pathway as the Bishop led the Princess down the drive and into Francis House. Father Thomas Mulheran, Director,

A royal entrance... Princess Diana is accompanied by Patrick Kelly, Bishop of Salford R.C. Diocese, Sister Aloysius, Margaret Hickie and other special guests

Chaplain and inspiration behind the hospice, greeted the Princess at the entrance.

She was presented with a posy of flowers by four-year-old Rebecca Byrom, accompanied by big brother Rory (7) and parents John and Dolores. The unpredictable nature of Rebecca's illness meant her role handing over a bouquet was uncertain until the last minute, but she performed the job admirably.

Her Royal Highness charmed everyone with her radiant smile and friendly attitude, quickly putting everyone at ease. She shared a genuine concern for each family, taking time and trouble to listen to their problems and hear what Francis House meant to them. Diana met as many guests as possible from various representative groups.

A small group of children played music as she passed by. Diana stopped for a photograph with them, looking beautiful in a red, green and white check suit. The Princess finally moved to the entrance hall where the official opening was completed with the unveiling of a commemorative plaque. She also placed her signature on the first page of the visitor book. Already well behind schedule, she ignored a request to get into the car and crossed the road to meet schoolchildren who had been waiting hours to see her.

Not only that, but the next day she telephoned the Lord Lieutenant's office asking for the name of the school so she could write and thank them for their patience. Her Royal Highness departed, cheered on her way by

Princess Diana meets Sir Matt Busby, the legendary Manchester United manager

delighted crowds. Back inside Francis House a warm and happy atmosphere pervaded as the care team set about giving respite care to one another as the kettle boiled yet again.

For Margaret Hickie it was a day to treasure. The royal visit came just a few months after she was appointed to lead the care team. Margaret recalled: 'We had a few children staying at the hospice and invited all the families on our books to come in for the day with their parents. We had the families in the lounge, with fundraisers stationed in different parts of the building.

'I showed Diana round the children's areas, while Sister Aloysius took her everywhere else. I introduced her to the families who loved her. She went up to the room of a boy with Batten's disease and his mum said she was lovely. Parents had been told in advance that they couldn't take pictures, but Diana said: 'Do you want a photo?' She then sat on the boy's bed and had her picture taken with him.'

One of the nurses, Natalie Hands, said: 'We had to be in our places quite a long time before she arrived. I was standing next to a mum whose daughter was quite severely disabled and couldn't move. The child was getting hot and bothered, so we plugged in a fan and turned her towards it. Suddenly Princess Diana came round the corner and shook our hands. She noticed the girl laid down on a long low trolley.

'Diana crouched down in a tight corner to see the child's face. All she had to do was walk round and shake hands, but she went out of her way where she couldn't really manoeuvre. It wasn't convenient for her, but she insisted on seeing the child. I also noticed that Diana's makeup was perfect.'

Martin Lochery was there in his capacity as a trustee. His next-door neighbour had a child at Francis House. Martin remembered: 'Diana spent quite a while with the mum and her daughter. Afterwards, we went back to our neighbours' house for a glass of wine. The girl's parents were very tearful, but so over the moon at such an amazing experience. The mum wrote to thank Diana who replied, and she now has that letter from Diana framed on the wall at home.'

Princess Diana's visit came at a time when her personal life was in turmoil with the break-up of her marriage to the then Prince Charles. Within six years she had died in a car crash in Paris. In the hospice newsletter, published in the autumn of 1997, Sister Aloysius paid a personal tribute to Princess Diana…

'I met Princess Diana only once in November 1991 – the day on which she officially opened Francis House. Within seconds we were both at ease, she was so much in tune with Francis House and what we were trying to do, there was little need for explanation.

'As she went from room to room, her interest was in those present rather than the building which had consumed our energies for 12 months and was all we wished it to be – her priorities were right. Much as her equerry tried to keep her to a timetable and I became conscious of his concern, it was obvious that Diana was not going to be rushed.

'She had come to meet the families and friends and encourage them, and this she did. While politely meeting guests and helpers, it was clear she wished to spend her time with the children and their parents. When before did a princess say: 'Hitch up and let me sit next to you.' It was obvious to all around that she only had eyes and ears for those families.

'Even at the very end of her visit when the police motorcycles were revving up to be away (she was by now late for her next appointment), she spotted children from a supporting school on the other side of the road and got out of the car to talk to them. Time didn't matter, children did, and they must not be disappointed.

'On entering Francis House there is now a plaque and photograph commemorating the occasion. Later in her troubled times when she was no longer HRH, I was asked if I intended to remove the photograph. I could only reply: 'No, the photograph will be here as long as Francis House is here. It is not here because of status, or position, but because of what Princess Diana brought to Francis House.

'She will always remain in our thoughts and prayers; for Francis House she truly is the People's Princess,' concluded the tribute from Sister Aloysius.

Friday, 14 October 2016

Like mother, like son. Some 25 years after Princess Diana opened Francis House, her elder son William was back to follow in her footsteps. The then Duke and Duchess of Cambridge officially opened Francis Lodge, a new wing of the hospice providing respite for young people over the age of 16.

William and Kate walked by a large photograph of the prince's late mother on the wall and William commented on how nice it was to have the family connection. Indeed, there was speculation that the then Earl and Countess of Wessex had been earmarked to perform the opening until William intervened and insisted he perform this particular royal engagement.

He wanted to visit Francis House himself as the hospice was so dear to the heart of his mother. Chief Executive, Revd David Ireland, and Director of Care, Gill Bevin, took the royal couple on a tour of the hospice before they ended their visit by unveiling a plaque to commemorate the official opening.

Appropriately, staff present at the hospice opening in 1991 were invited to the big day. They included Clinical Lead Natalie Hands; Monsignor Tom Mulheran; chef Dean Jenkins; receptionist Carmel Holland; Sister Austin; long-serving nurse Jackie Graham and nurse Pat Whitehead.

David said at the time:

> *'This was a really special occasion for Francis House. It was 25 years to the month since Princess Diana opened Francis House. So it felt extremely fitting that her son, Prince William, officially opened Francis Lodge and set us off on the next stage of our journey.'*

Just like his mother, William and Kate met children cared for by the hospice. Among them was Angel, a visually impaired five-year-old who was born with encephalocele, a

Prince William chats to Sharon Nelson and her daughter Angel

A smiling royal couple make their way through Francis House

condition that affects the brain. Mum, Sharon Nelson, was alongside her. Fiona Sweeney and son Josh, who had spinal cancer, also met the VIP guests. Josh said:

> *'It was amazing them being here. It's so good to have been invited to Francis House. Kate was really nice and kind.'*

Fiona said: 'They were so down to earth. They just make you feel so comfortable. It's not like they think they're better than you. They're just lovely. It was just like speaking to anyone else, which I didn't expect. Josh felt really comfortable. The Duchess was great with him.'

The couple met Chair of Trustees Chris Roberts, Francis Lodge Clinical Lead Tracey Potts and those who laid the Francis Lodge foundation stones, including Dame Sarah Storey and her husband Barney. Kate Snape, who has received care from Francis House for many years, was also in the welcoming party. Natalie Hands has great memories of that special visit.

She said: 'As I was retiring, David asked if I'd like to be in reception to meet them as they arrived. William was just like Diana and very

Nice to meet you… Kate enjoying her visit

chatty. One child was getting a little noisy and his mum was uncomfortable. I opened the door to a tiny side room to give her some privacy and so she could still see what was going on through the glass.

'As the child was being settled, William and Kate saw what was happening. They didn't want the mum to feel awkward and spent time with her. As they left, William and Kate made eye contact. He gave her this look as if to say: "Are you okay?" They had heard many upsetting stories. She gave him a reassuring look. I was really impressed with both of them.'

David Ireland remembered: 'William and Kate separated to make sure that they spoke to every family there.' An abiding memory is a minor panic over a security sweep, a routine procedure for royal visits. David said: 'The police were busy conducting other checks so only arrived 45 minutes before William and Kate. It was late morning and the police asked for our maintenance man Keith so he could lift manholes. I explained he'd been here since 9am waiting for them to arrive and they hadn't turned up. I said he'd gone to put his best suit on to meet William and wouldn't be lifting manholes now. I said: "You'll have to do it yourself."'

An informal visit to Francis House was made by the Duchess of Norfolk on Friday, 24 July 1992, in her capacity as joint chair of Help the Hospices. The Duchess was also a patron of Francis House.

CHAPTER 3

SISTERS TO THE RESCUE

The Sisters had packed their bags and left their convent to make way for Francis House. Giving up their home was a selfless act by the so-called Rescue Sisters of the Franciscan Missionaries of St Joseph. They had relinquished their congregational way of life in Didsbury.

Their religious vows included a promise to serve the needs of society. By forfeiting their home, they were fulfilling God's wish. Among those leaving Our Lady of Lourdes Convent were Sister Philomena FMSJ and Sister Joan FMSJ.

Sister Philomena and Sister Joan

The two Sisters did not move far when they vacated the premises on Monday, 10 December 1990. In fact, they went only a matter of yards down the driveway to make way for Francis

The Rescue Sisters of the Franciscan Missionaries of St Joseph

Work underway to build Francis House Children's Hospice

House. Both took up residence in a house owned by the Rescue Society in the same grounds on Parrswood Road. Moving there also was Sister Austin FMSJ who joined the Francis House team where she became such an integral part of its operations.

Most of the remaining Sisters dispersed into two other houses in the Salford Diocese to continue their work with the Catholic Children's Rescue Society. Sisters Philomena and Joan lived in the premises at the gateway to Francis House for some years, before eventually moving elsewhere within Salford R.C. Diocese. Incidentally, the last of the Franciscan Sisters finally vacated the site in 2022 after almost a century of work in Didsbury.

The convent was converted to make way for the hospice in 1990, but the Society offices remained within the Parrswood Road complex for several years. Sister Joan recalled: 'There were very different reactions from the Sisters at having to leave the convent. We were lucky – there were about five of us who were asked to go to live in the house on the corner. But other Sisters had to move to another place, and it was harder for them.

'We were delighted that a children's hospice was being built. More so because the whole family was being included. Francis House was caring for the parents of the disabled child as well as the child coming in for respite. It was a great facility, especially as there weren't many children's hospices around. They weren't subsidised by the government so had to constantly fundraise to maintain their work.'

As a voluntary agency, the Rescue Society helped different communities around Greater Manchester. Sisters Philomena and Joan were involved in its fostering and adoption work, some of which centred around prevention. That meant trying to keep the child in the family home. The Society's family placement work had highlighted the need for further assistance for children with a short life expectancy.

Joan added: 'My work for the Rescue Society involved preventing children going into care if possible. I then went on to the family placement team and had a different focus looking after children in residential care and placing them with families. Our work was all over the diocese which covers a large area so we saw the need for Francis House.

'Sister Aloysius was the prime mover in getting the hospice built. She recognised very early on that there was a gap in services. Families with children with disabilities living at home needed respite and the children also needed respite from parents. The hospice was a separate organisation altogether from the Rescue Society. We didn't go in and out of Francis House. Understandably, they wanted to keep it private. They were caring for families and children with life-limiting disabilities and didn't want people coming and going.'

Sister Philomena's links with the Rescue Society go back to 1956 when she undertook social work training. She said: 'I was part of the adoption team. Babies were brought by mothers, and they stayed in the nursery for a short period of time until placed for adoption. The birth mother could visit and adoptive parents were introduced to the child. They spent time with them to build up a relationship before taking the baby home. The fostering unit was set up after the adoption service.'

The role of Monsignor Gerard McCormack, secretary to the Rescue Society from 1955 until 1977, should not be underestimated in the development of child welfare. Sister Philomena said: 'Father McCormack wanted to close the large orphanages and put children into small homes, or units. He wanted to turn off the tap of admitting children into care.

'He wanted them to stay with their birth families with help from the Rescue Society. Father McCormack developed a very good family welfare team to help parents care for children who ordinarily would have been taken into care due to ill-treatment or for other reasons. So, there was emphasis on preventative work, keeping children with families with support in their own home. If the child couldn't stay with their own family, they would be received into the care of the local authority and placed with us.

'The Rescue Society bought houses close to Francis House. A large orphanage on the Parrswood site closed and children moved into homes for smaller groups. Father McCormack was a tremendous person. He said we're going to close these big institutions and have more family life within a residential setting. More one-to-one care rather than in big groups.

'He wanted to stop children being left with

Monsignor Gerard McCormack

no care plan for them. Many were left because the mother, or the single parent, couldn't cope. They said they would come back for the child but never did and he wanted that stopped. If the child was coming into care, there would be a continuous plan for that child's future.'

Father McCormack died in 1978, a year after handing over the secretarial reins to Monsignor Thomas Mulheran. Father Tom then realised that the homes were struggling to cope looking after children with complex needs. Jim Buggy was a member of the Rescue Society family welfare team and had worked for the local authority.

Sister Philomena added: 'We couldn't meet the needs of severely disabled children. Specialist care was required, whereas many of our staff were trained for residential care which wasn't sufficient to provide the level of attention these children needed. We wouldn't have been able to provide for the mother and father. There just wasn't room and the focus was on the family. It was important the family were cared for as well as the child with a disability.

'We were thrilled with the work Francis House did with children. Yes, we had feelings about moving out of the convent, but we got over that. I'd done a lot of work on children's rights. My focus was on a child's right to good care, nurturing and family life if possible. Whether it was with their own birth family

or their adoptive family. The child was the priority and I felt that was being fulfilled totally at Francis House.

'The hospice was totally different to the Rescue Society. The ethos was different, the constitution was different. It was a separate organisation, but it grew from the moral obligation we, as a Rescue Society, felt we had to provide as a service for disabled children.

'There weren't many Sisters involved in Francis House initially. It was Sister Aloysius, Sister Austin, Sister Francine and Sister Maureen. We continued to work for the Rescue Society in the adoption and fostering section. There, we always called ourselves the A team because we felt we were an excellent team.'

Sister Maureen

The role of Sister Aloysius as co-founder of Francis House has been well documented over the years. But less well known is a defining moment in the charity's history which involved her colleague Jim Buggy, a senior social worker. For it was Jim who came up with the idea in the first place to create a children's hospice in south Manchester.

It was his suggestion which eventually led to the religious Sisters giving up their convent on Parrswood Road, in Didsbury. Among them Sister Maureen FMSJ, whose passion for nursing and caring for sick children and young adults has not diminished more

than 30 years on. Sister Maureen is the only original so-called Rescue Sister who is still actively working in Didsbury.

She has a fascinating insight into the sequence of events that led to the conversion of Our Lady of Lourdes Convent into a children's hospice where she is still involved to this day. Sister Maureen was there to hear Sister Aloysius inform the Sisters that there was a possibility the convent – their home – might be needed for other purposes.

That fateful meeting on Thursday, 1 February 1990 might not even have happened without a chance conversation between Monsignor Thomas Mulheran, secretary of the Catholic Children's Rescue Society, and

Francis House stalwart Sister Maureen FMSJ

Jim, who had been recruited from Manchester City Council where he was held in high esteem for his long-standing work with children with special needs. His work formed part of the Society's fostering and adoption activities.

Sister Maureen explained: 'What I learned afterwards, and Father Tom told the story too, was that Father was in his office forward planning with Jim Buggy. Jim turned to Father Tom and said: "What we need in Manchester is a children's hospice like Helen House, in Oxford."

'At that time no one had heard of a children's hospice. They knew of St Ann's, an adult hospice in Heald Green, but hadn't heard of a children's hospice. Father Tom was listening to him and, in effect, was really listening to what God was saying. That's how it worked, through Jim.

'Something must have resonated and Father Tom called Sister Aloysius through from her office down the corridor to sit and listen to what Jim was saying. My understanding is that Sister Aloysius was actually given the task of looking into the possibility of a children's hospice, as Father Tom had a lot of work to do here.

'I was training to be a nurse and lived at the convent, while other Sisters lived and worked outside in the community. Father

Sister Maureen showing off her footballing skills

Tom was our chaplain and we had Mass every day in the chapel. Sister Aloysius didn't live here but worked here in the Catholic Rescue offices on the same site as the convent.

'At the start of February, they just said there's a meeting and Sister Aloysius would like to talk to all of us in the evening and it's about Mount Carmel. We came along to the meeting, which was the first I'd heard about it. I can picture her in the big room.

'She explained they were thinking of starting a hospice for sick children and if they obtained approval were thinking of using the convent.

'I was a young Sister and we were sent all over the place. We lived out of suitcases anyway and I'd lived in different places. So, for me, I can honestly say I didn't mind moving out.

'You'd have to ask the other Sisters, but I don't think moving out was a big issue.

'What attracted me to joining the convent was Rescue work, which I loved. But I wasn't sure it was quite right for me. I loved nursing, though, and thought: "Wow, this is my dream." The next morning, I asked Sister Aloysius if I could be on the staff, as a nurse, if the plans went ahead.

'Father Tom had breakfast in his office as usual after Mass and I said to him: "I love this idea. Can I be part of it?" He smiled and said: "Welcome on board," or something like that. The decision about the hospice had to go to the Rescue Council. I was a staff nurse at Wythenshawe Hospital and on the day it was decided – 8 March, 1990 – I remember I was on the early shift. I got off the bus after work

and ran straight to Sister's office and asked: "What did the Rescue Council say?"'

'She said: "Yes, it's going ahead." I had completed my three-year RGN general nursing training and spent 12 months undertaking consolidation training at Wythenshawe. That ended in the summer of 1990 when I also took my final vows.

'Sister Aloysius asked me to find out what training I needed to work in the hospice. She also arranged for Jim, Sister Theresa, who was in charge at the convent, and me to visit Martin House in Yorkshire. That was the only children's hospice in the north and they'd been most supportive. I spoke to their nurses who advised me to take a children's nursing course. Jim kindly enrolled me on a 60-week course that September at Crumpsall Hospital. The course finished in November 1991 when I came to Francis House, having just qualified.'

Sister Maureen was quick to spread the word about the new hospice during the training period. While on placement at Booth Hall, she met Margaret Hickie, and informed her that an exciting new hospice was on the horizon. That conversation ultimately led to Margaret, a vastly experienced healthcare professional, becoming Head of Care and Registered Manager, a post she held with distinction until retiring in 2009.

Sister Maureen explained: 'I was on a health visitor placement and Margaret worked in the same office. Everyone would ask what my plans were and I told her about the hospice. In fact, every ward I went on I was telling the nurses so I was recruiting as I went along.' Sister Maureen gained a distinction in her final exam, thanks to her comprehensive essay about terminal illness and respite care in children's hospices.

Sister Maureen still has that study work in her possession as a souvenir. In fact, it features in presentations she delivers about Francis House and its origins. 'The presentation was written in 2003 at the request of Sister Aloysius. It's about our background, how we started and hospice care. It has a day in the life of the hospice, our different kinds of care and how we've grown.'

It also references the well-known 'Rescuing Hug' story about twin baby girls born prematurely in the United States. The midwife put them both in an incubator. The well child put her arm around her sick sister who duly survived and thrived. 'It's a tear-jerker. One of our volunteers gave me that story to tell. It's about the power of love and touch and in some ways reflects Francis House,' said Sister Maureen.

> **Maybe fate saw the convent converted into a children's hospice. Sister Maureen recalls an anecdote which suggests that was the destiny of the building. 'The priest before Father Tom was Father McCormack. A story passed on to me is that one day he looked across from his office to the convent and said: "That won't always be a convent, it'll be something else." He had a vision, but he didn't know what.'**

Father McCormack died in 1978, long before the changes occurred. Sister Maureen moved back from Rochdale to a house on the corner by the hospice to start her coveted new job. 'I had been for visits and seen it grow, but it was still a work in progress and the chapel wasn't finished. It was total luxury with beautiful surroundings.'

Sister Maureen has devoted more than three decades to Francis House. As well as a lifetime spent nursing sick children, she helped supervise volunteers at the charity for a spell. She was one of the Sisters asked to change their congregational way of life, her colleagues moving into other smaller houses to offer ministry to local communities.

Sister Maureen has divided her time between Francis House and the residential home at 463, formerly Mount Carmel. The ethos is the same at all Francis House facilities, including another residential unit located at 92 Barcicroft Road, in Heaton Moor, which opened in February 2023. Sister Maureen embodies that ethos. She is part of the hospice's heritage, though modestly plays down her immense contribution.

But Sister Maureen was there at the beginning and has led from the front ever since, treating youngsters as part of her duties to God. The founders of Francis House whom she knew so well would be proud of her faith and devotion.

CHAPTER 4

RELIEF AT LAST FOR FAMILIES

With Francis House open, a young mother described the relief felt by families for whom the burden had suddenly been eased. The children's hospice had more than 30 referrals within the first month. Respite help was at last available for mums and dads who were providing round-the-clock care to their loved ones.

Mother and Son Relax at Last

The mother of a young boy – one of the first children welcomed into Francis House – summed up her emotions:

'I was relieved of cooking and washing while watching every breath of my child. I felt almost disbelief at getting an unbroken night's sleep, being able to rise at leisure and have a late breakfast. I knew that my son had been washed and dressed, had enjoyed his breakfast and was now happily occupied. I was free to take a walk, browse shops and return to enjoy a relaxed hour with my son before sharing a beautifully prepared lunch.'

Little everyday things most of us just take for granted. But when someone has been deprived of them for so long, these simple experiences took on a completely new meaning.

The mum was relaxed and so was her contented child. Both returned home feeling refreshed and looking forward to their next stay at Francis House.

In the event, some 25 families suffering similar anxieties were cared for in the first three months, with referrals coming from several sources, including social workers and Macmillan nurses. The length of stay varied from just a few hours up to 10 days.

Chef Dean Jenkins and kitchen volunteers at Francis House in the early days

The first edition of the charity newsletter Rainbow News was hot off the press just before Christmas 1991. The front page displayed a big picture of a smiling Princess Diana meeting children and families at the official opening a few weeks earlier. Inside the edition, there was an insight into the staff room, just as the care team had been ready to roll out the welcome mat for other VIP guests ... the first families! The story read:

'At the start of the orientation week, Head of Care Margaret Hickie was faced with 15 eager and willing staff of various ages and experiences and the task of creating a team par excellence. Gone are the uniforms. Gone is the professional status. Gone is the security of routine and set procedures.

'In its place we have a relaxed informality with a cosy, homely atmosphere for the children and their families in a most lovely setting. Over the weeks we have developed a deepening friendship, a genuine concern for each other's welfare and a sharing of inter-personal skills.

'The whole concept of Francis House, caring for children with a short life expectancy and respite care for the family, is a new and challenging role for all of us and we feel privileged to be at the beginning. As the months pass, no doubt we will face difficult times. Overwork and over emotion, requiring counselling, possibly outside help, heaven sent or otherwise. Should this occasion arise we are sure the support will be there, enabling us to supply the very special needs of Francis House.'

There were two deaths at Francis House in the first few weeks. One was a two-week-old baby, whose parents greatly appreciated the care team support provided afterwards. The couple were allowed time on their own to grieve in the family accommodation.

The condition of children referred varied greatly. Most were neurological and progressive. Some had cancer, while one little girl had Aids. The care team started regular monthly meetings with local community nurses and Macmillan staff. Relationships were forged with other agencies including The Christie in nearby Withington.

The outreach service also went into action, with care staff visiting families at home and one boy at school. Families reacted positively. All found the hospice hugely relaxing. One family went to Mass in the hospice chapel each Sunday even when their child was not in residence.

In the first six months until May 1992, Francis House received 90 referrals. Slowly but surely word was spreading about the merits of respite care for children and, crucially, how it was designed for the whole family. Not just mum and dad, but brothers and sisters as well.

● ● ●

Francis House was presented with two large vehicles to take children on outings. A Nissan Prairie and a Volkswagen Caravelle were converted to carry wheelchairs. The Nissan was donated by the Alexandra Hospital in Cheadle and the Volkswagen by staff at McVitie's biscuit factory. Small groups of children were suddenly able to visit places previously inaccessible to them.

The early care team. Far left, Sister Maureen with Jackie Graham fifth from the right

Unbelievably, the Nissan was stolen in April 1992. It was never recovered and had seemingly been stolen to order and taken out of the country. Brotherwood, the Somerset-based company which had carried out the initial conversion, produced a replacement vehicle within six weeks. Insurers Cornhill also acted quickly to ensure minimum delay.

A hospice neighbour so incensed by the theft offered to have an immobiliser installed, a kind gesture the charity accepted. Days out soon became a regular occurrence, either to shops, country parks, museums, galleries, Manchester Airport and Jodrell Bank.

The aim was to enhance the life of sick children who otherwise might miss out on trips out due to their intense care needs. Specialist equipment, including portable respirators, were invaluable to allow these special visits to go ahead. The days out offered time for the families, a precious commodity. Excursions, whether to the seaside or the zoo, were organised with flexibility in mind to the best advantage of each individual family.

By the time Francis House celebrated its third birthday in November 1994, some 180 children had used the hospice. The figure would rise steadily, vindicating the shrewd but brave decision to go ahead and build the hospice.

●●●

The cost of running Francis House was always a concern for Sister Aloysius and her staff. There was no financial help from the government, with local health authorities contributing a tiny fraction of the funds needed to run the charity. The staff ratio was high, a necessity due to the chronic problems of the children in their care.

In the 1991–92 financial year – the period Francis House opened – salaries were £218,000, some 72 per cent of total costs of £300,000. Revenue costs were forecast to rise to £670,000 in the first full year of operations, 1992–93, with wages and pension contributions amounting to £500,000, around three quarters of the total costs.

As the hospice became more popular, costs were only going to increase, especially as the cost of living was also rising. Appeals were made to potential donors – corporate or otherwise – to try to persuade them to fund specific items. The actual capital cost was £1.5m, compared to an original budget of £1m. This is a breakdown of costs:

Chapel £100,000	Lift £57,829
Lounge £45,482	Kitchen £42,160
Parents' ground floor flat £61,000	First floor £28,500
Dining Room £25,857	Hydrotherapy Room £32,688
Mortuary £28,533	Bathrooms £27,880
Gas equipment £27,265	Laundry room £23,895
Reception £23,403	Children's bedrooms £18,500
Hobbies room/music room £16,500	Offices £15,049
Treatment room £9,502	Quiet room £8,088
Parker Bath plus hoist £5,196	Generator £1,000

Francis House stressed the important difference between an adult and a children's hospice. Adult hospices usually admit inpatients for the last few weeks of their lives. Day care facilities are also provided for adults with life-limiting illnesses who may still live for quite some time. A children's hospice was an entirely different concept.

The purpose was to provide respite for the whole family and to enable the family to continue caring for their child with a terminal illness at home for as long as possible.

Parents can stay with the child at Francis House or leave them there in the care of staff. Either way, the parents would be refreshed and revitalised after enjoying the luxury of a full night's sleep, with no washing or cooking if staying at the hospice. Parents would have time to spend with their other children and with each other.

The life of a family with a child with a limited life expectancy became severely restricted. They hardly ever had a night of undisturbed sleep and could not plan a holiday. They found it difficult to leave their child with a babysitter and invariably could not give enough time to their well children.

Early hospice archives documenting the experiences of families reported that friends often found it difficult to be 'as normal' with parents of sick children and, as a result, visited them less often. Not because they were bad friends, but they could not cope with the pain they saw.

How many of us would be the same? What do you say to a couple who have heard the shattering news that their child might not live for very long? That there is no known cure for their medical condition. The original meaning of the word hospice is 'a place of rest and refreshment on a journey.' So Francis House would provide a haven for a child and family together in a comfortable environment, surrounded by caring and qualified staff. There they could meet other parents and children in similar situations.

● ● ●

Here is a sample of comments from parents during the early years.

'On my first visit to Francis House I stood outside the door and cried. It seemed like admitting defeat. I had looked after him all this time and now I'm needing help. If only I had known. As soon as the door opened a wall of love surrounded me and everything changed. I just wish I had found it sooner.'

'From the start we could tell that Francis House was a place where our family would be comfortable in a homely and caring environment and our daughter Karen would have all the care she needed. Our three children loved Francis House from the beginning. They had plenty to do and were able to have some fun. Simon and I were able to share our problems with the staff and have a rest, safe in the knowledge that our daughter was in very capable hands. Francis House and its splendid staff have given us all friendship,

comfort and emotional support through a very painful time in our lives. As a family we continue to pay regular visits and value the special friendships we have made. Our only regret is that we did not know about this wonderful place sooner.'

'We felt awful leaving Kirsty at first but the staff make you feel like you're at home and you can do what you want, when you want. If Kirsty is uncomfortable in the night they'll see to her – it makes such a difference just to get a good night's sleep. Kirsty enjoys it because she gets so much input – we wouldn't let her go anywhere else.

'We are happy here and we know Kirsty is happy.

'When I found out my daughter was disabled, I didn't know how I was going to cope. Coming here and seeing the other children and their families gave me the feeling that I wasn't alone and that I could cope. Being able to speak to other parents and get their advice is really helpful. Satveer needs 24-hour care so Francis House gives me a chance to spend time with my two other girls.'

'We can't describe what Francis House means to us. It just means so much. When we're at home we don't go out. We go out with the boys, but Eddie and I don't have any time to ourselves. Coming here is like coming home. As soon as we come in, we feel the stress starting to lift. It's a total care package, including parents.'

Integral to the total care package is support in areas such as siblings, homecare, bereavement and emotional care. In 1993, the home and bereavement support units were developed further. Staff at the heart of providing these essential services have spoken in detail about their value elsewhere in this book. Home visits offered practical help in the form of nursing care for a sick child, relieving parents and the family so they could go out for a few hours and spend precious time together.

It can be quite an emotional experience for the family of a sick child when they are introduced to Francis House for the first time.

The homecare team goes out to see the family upon referral and that first meeting can be difficult. It's another reminder for the parent that their child is now quite seriously ill and they've got a life-limiting condition.

They find out what help is available and it is further acknowledgement that their child is taking another step towards the end of their life. Everything is done at the family's pace and on their terms. They are told about Francis House and what it can do for them. The next stage is a visit to the hospice.

They come in for a meal and have a look around. They see the Rainbow Room where children go following their death. The homecare team visits homes and hospitals to assist families. Some families may never go out for weeks between visits to Francis House, while many children cannot be left with just anyone because of their clinical needs.

●●●

The emotional support service started in 2009 and is offered to young people aged 13 and over who use the hospice and have life-limiting conditions. Bereavement support had been offered for some time before it was recognised that there was little emotional support available for teenagers and adults. Sessions take place in Francis Lodge, at home or in places like coffee shops. A room known

as the Pod is equipped with audio visual equipment, enabling video messages to be recorded for parents.

●●●

The first bereavement day was held on Saturday, 14 May 1994. It was known as Rainbow Day and later renamed Memory Day. It was designed for families whose child had died since the opening of Francis House. Families of 77 children came together for a time of remembrance.

The day began with families and the care team meeting before a midday service in the chapel followed by a buffet lunch. There was time for parents and families to reminisce, while children were entertained by the care team during the afternoon.

One of the first bereavement days, known as Rainbow Day and later renamed Memory Day

Staff approached the day with trepidation, anxious how it would be received. In the event, it was an overwhelming success and became a popular annual tradition at Francis House. All families react to the loss of their child differently. Each child and their circumstances are unique to them.

Some would be very close to their loss, while others might be further along the grief path. Yet it was hoped each family took away something that provided comfort and hope for them. By the end of the afternoon, everyone was shattered but happily so. It was hoped all families felt a sense of peace, despite the emotional toll of the day.

That first Rainbow Day was a poignant occasion: the one day when bereaved parents could spend time with their memories in a protective environment before returning to everyday life.

Bereavement support was handled on a more informal basis initially until it was consolidated and became more specialised. Regular contact was made with families, either through visits or phone calls. Birthdays and anniversaries were remembered and the family were invited to coffee mornings three or four times a year.

These were more social occasions for parents to meet, talk and support each other. There was a wish, though, that the support could be developed and that proved to be the case. Jeannie Bratton, Pat Fidler and Natalie Hands were at the forefront of this progress.

●●●

Sibling support was also at the core of hospice activities. In 1994, staff devised ways of making visits to Francis House an even happier and fuller experience for brothers and sisters, allowing more relaxation time for tired parents. Around 90 brothers and sisters had visited or had contact with the hospice by this stage.

Staff worked together to improve play facilities and develop closer relationships with the children. They planned more general activities in the hospice and separate age group events. Play volunteers were recruited, each responsible to a member of the care team. They spent part of the day helping occupy energetic well children who, when not out in the garden, parks or places of interest, were in the playroom and the ever-popular art/messy room.

Their efforts were highly successful. The extra help meant the art room was always prepared for use, with creative work prominently displayed. The play volunteers enjoyed outings with children and they added a greatly needed, and appreciated, extra pair of hands. The late Jeannie Bratton, from the care team, recounted an occasion enjoyed by younger children.

'Christopher ran in to join the party. He was very excited and had looked forward to it for ages. The party was a Teddy Bears' picnic held in the hall of Francis House. It was just for the young brothers and sisters of children who use the hospice. Christopher ran to meet his friends whom he knew from previous visits. His mum confided that he always looked forward to coming to the hospice because he knew he was going to enjoy himself.

'Christopher had recently shared the sadness of his sister's death with staff. He knew we understood and were always happy to talk to him about her. Much work had gone into preparing the Teddy Bears' picnic and the laughter of the children made it all worthwhile.'

The next venture for the support group for brothers and sisters was a weekend camp for older children. After such a good start, staff were encouraged by the response they had received and looked forward to continuing an excellent service of love, care and fun for these important children.

Sibling support for bereaved brothers and sisters later became known as Shining Stars. The Seasons group was formed for siblings of children still using Francis House. The team helps brothers and sisters realise they are not alone in facing the problems associated with having a sick brother or sister. Specialist staff who have assisted in all these support services have recounted their experiences elsewhere in this book.

Facilities Early On

The image often conjured up by the word hospice is one of long, dark corridors lined with beds, a misplaced perception that was dispelled by Francis House from the outset. The hospice lounge was light, airy and homely, giving the appearance and atmosphere of a large, happy family home.

A place filled with laughter, music and the chatter of excited children and an abundance of colour. Each bedroom was decorated in the colours of the rainbow, making them bright and cheerful. All had an extra bed for anyone wanting to stay with their child. Accommodation comprised two family flats – one with two double beds, the other with three double beds.

The hospice offered accommodation for up to seven children and their families at any one time. The criteria for entering the hospice was that the child had an illness from which they were not expected to recover and was under 16 at point of referral. The main lounge in Francis House was open-plan with a large kitchen, sitting room and dining room, designed to make families feel at home. The hydrotherapy pool was a big attraction and offered a soothing place of relaxation for children and exhausted parents.

Willing volunteers were on hand, whether in the kitchen or care team, supporting the highly qualified specialist nursing care team. Special equipment enabled children to spend their time in Francis House as pain free as possible. Medical and pharmaceutical cover was provided by the local GP practice and a local pharmacist, together with support from local paediatric units and community paediatric nurses. The Rainbow Room comprised a bedroom and lounge, a special facility for the parents of a child who had died, allowing them the time they needed to come to terms with their loss.

Six months after Francis House opened, the builders were still on site. Further improvements were taking place. A building at the end of the garden, consisting of a hall, offices, garages and toilets, was in poor

Early care team members Judith Higgins (left) and Alison Pardoe pay a return visit on an Open Day

condition. Ideally, the work would have been carried out as part of the initial project, but it had to be delayed due to limited funds.

An estimate of £335,000 supplied by Eric Wright Construction some two years earlier was honoured by the firm. The renovation included two additional bedrooms for parents, a hall, workshop and storeroom. Work started in May 1992 and was completed four months later.

A two-storey unit with three upstairs flats for parents was built as part of the next phase a few years later when a soft play area, teenage lounge and music room were added. The music room was opened by the famous Irish flautist James Galway, a good friend of Sister Aloysius. His brother George was a neighbour of the hospice, living in Didsbury, and taught music. James – known as the man with the

golden flute – allowed one of the care staff, herself a talented flautist, to play his musical instrument at the opening.

The music room was important to Francis House. A trained music therapist encouraged children to express themselves whatever their limit. Children improvise music to suit their breathing, movement or a favourite topic. The response from the child can be anything from vocals, a tap on a tambourine or a movement. This response encourages communication and expression. The music room was filled with instruments, including specialist equipment which responded to movement.

Elsewhere, the Snoezelen room was specially designed to stimulate the senses of severely disabled children. Coloured lights, different textures, gentle music and sounds enabled children to relax in a safe, stimulating environment. The arts and craft room was well-stocked with equipment for art, craft and sculpture. Painting, printing, colouring-in – for youngest to oldest – has been a popular pastime, with all children creating their own masterpiece.

> The teenage room was a haven for adolescents. All teenagers need their own space, and this special room allowed freedom to play music, watch videos or just sit and chat in peace. Special weekends were organised during the year when Francis House was taken over by teenagers who had the run of the building ... within reason!

The computer room was for work or play – the choice was theirs. Whether they wanted to surf the world wide web or play computer games, they had the facilities and the opportunity. A child and adolescent therapist worked with the children through play. It enabled them to work through difficult and painful emotions relating to life-limiting conditions, pre-bereavement and death. The therapeutic service offered individual specialised support to children and their families. A dedicated, well-equipped playroom ensured privacy and confidentiality.

Aromatherapy was offered to some children or family members by an experienced therapist. Treatments ranged from relaxing and de-stressing to uplifting and revitalising. Massage of specific body areas eased aches and pains, with medical permission required if necessary. Francis House had the luxury of large, enclosed gardens with play equipment designed to fit wheelchairs, so all the children visiting could experience outdoor play.

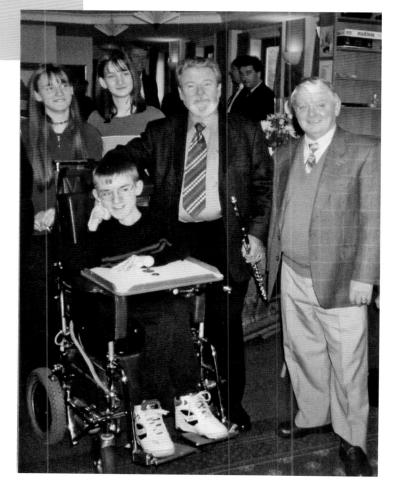

Famous flautist James Galway and his brother George on a visit to the hospice

Name Change and Subsidiary

The symbol of a rainbow has always featured in the Francis House emblem but the word rainbow was removed from the charity's title in 2012. Instead of the Rainbow Family Trust, it became Francis House Family Trust.

Chief Executive David Ireland explained the move. He said: 'We changed the name because Francis House had become the known brand but kept our logo because it's got the family in it and is so recognisable. The family is at the centre of everything we do here. The rainbow is the symbol of hope for people of different faiths and none – something good in stormy times.'

Francis House Family Trust operates Francis House and Francis Lodge. However, a trading subsidiary known as Francis House Families Ltd. runs the two residential units called 463 and 92. The company receives funding

The residential unit at 92 Barcicroft Road

The opening of the six-bed unit at Barcicroft Road in February 2023

Ann Langshaw (left) and Vicky Marsh outside 463 Parrswood Road

Road, which opened in February 2023, is a six-bed unit. It also accommodates teens and young adults with even more complex clinical needs and limited capacity.

Both homes are essential. Youngsters are now living into their twenties, or even thirties, due to recent medical interventions. Often their care falls in large part on parents, placing great stress on these families. Many parents become ill themselves and are unable to give the care needed. Sadly, a significant number die before their sick children.

Unfortunately, facilities which can care for young people with these conditions are few and far between and many young people are placed in nursing homes for the elderly.

through individual care packages. The 463 property on Parrswood Road was purchased from Caritas Diocese of Salford in 2015 and opened as a seven-bed 'home for life' for teenagers and young adults already on the Francis House roll. Number 92 on Barcicroft

FRANCIS HOUSE FAMILY TRUST
Philosophy

The philosophy of the Francis House Family Trust and Francis House Children's Hospice flows from the belief in the sanctity of life and the dignity of the person. Francis House exists for the provision of appropriate care for children with life-threatening conditions and the necessary support and short-term rest for their families. The hospice movement is concerned with the process of dying and with bereavement.

While it is true that hospices have usually been founded by people of a specific faith, the service that a hospice seeks to offer always respects the understanding, vision and attitude to life and death of the person and family who seek help in the crisis which they face.

Francis House seeks to offer children and their families this very special service. Whereas hospitals must focus on the curing of those who are ill, the hospice focus is on the care of those for whom a cure is unlikely. Medical and all other support will be centred on comfort and quality of care and death with dignity. This is the specific vision which Francis House will seek to share with all families who use its services.

To avoid that happening, Francis House expanded its services, creating 463 and 92. Each property consists of two semi-detached homes knocked into one.

Identifying them only by their street number is deliberate. Most residential addresses are known by number only. This is no different, while a brand name might feel institutional. 463 was known as Mount Carmel previously and had been a respite centre for children with severe disabilities.

The offices of the Catholic Children's Rescue Society on the Parrswood Road site were in use until April 2012. The Society ceased its adoption work due to changes in government legislation and became Caritas Diocese of Salford. Today it helps those experiencing poverty, disadvantage and discrimination.

National Lottery Impact

Manchester's only children's hospice is facing its own fight for survival – over funding. That was the introduction to a story in the *Manchester Evening News* late in 1996. Francis House had seen a huge drop in income since the start of the National Lottery two years earlier.

Francis House in the news amid an uncertain financial future

Fight for children's hospice

By Kevin Feddy

MANCHESTER children's hospice is facing a survival battle because its income has slumped by £400,000 since the National Lottery began.

Francis House in Didsbury has suffered a 20 per cent drop in two years. The decline has delivered a hammer blow to the Rainbow Family Trust which runs it.

It relies almost totally on well-wishers and needs £3,000 a day to continue.

It has had a bid for a National Lottery Charities Board grant refused.

Fund-raiser Kate Puć said today: 'We are 99.9 per cent reliant on donations. We receive nothing from the government and only a small amount from health authorities.

'As well as running costs we need to repay a £1m loan taken out to build the hospice. We have cared for more than 350 children since it was opened by Princess Diana in 1991.

'In the last financial year we were £200,000 down. We have improved a little this year, but we have to recruit full-time fund-raisers to achieve that, and that has incurred higher costs.

'We have been able to offer fantastic prizes like a Caribbean cruise for £1 a ticket but people walk past to buy Lottery tickets. We have been refused a grant from the Charities board but we have submitted another bid. I hope we are successful. I can think of no better cause than the care of terminally ill children, yet so much of the Lottery proceeds seems to go on art and heritage projects.'

A spokeswoman for Camelot which runs the Lottery said: 'As a company, we have always said the most effective way of giving to charities is to give it directly – not to play the Lottery.'

A spokesman for the National Lotteries Charities Board said the next round of grants – totalling more than £100m – would be decided within two weeks and would go to organisations involved in health, disability and care.

The story told how the centre, which relies almost entirely on donations, needs £3,000 a day to continue with its valuable work, but has suffered a 17 per cent drop in income in the last two years.

Fundraiser Kate Puć said:

'Fewer than four per cent of our income comes from public funding. This, plus the impact of the National Lottery on all charities, means we are surviving hand-to-mouth at present.'

The hospice, which had just celebrated its fifth birthday, said cash was urgently needed in order to reach its sixth birthday.

Kate added: 'We've cared for more than 350 children since the hospice was opened by Princess Diana in 1991. In the last financial year, we were £200,000 down. We've improved a little this year but have had to recruit full-time fundraisers to achieve that, incurring higher costs.

'I've seen the impact of the National Lottery myself while selling raffle tickets. We've been able to offer fantastic prizes like a Caribbean cruise for a £1 ticket, but people walk past to buy Lottery tickets. We applied for a grant, but this was unsuccessful. I can think of no better cause than the care of terminally ill children, yet so much of Lottery proceeds seem to go on art and heritage projects.'

Thankfully, the hospice survived and the incredible Kirsty Howard Appeal a few years later would provide a massive £5m injection of funds to change the financial picture. As Francis House reached its 10th anniversary in 2001, the charity was still desperate for support. At this stage it was unaware the Kirsty factor was about to provide a lifeline. An appeal for help went out to businesses and individuals. The message read:

'For the last 10 years Francis House has been the ray of light in the lives of more than 500 terminally ill children and their families. The support provided by the staff and carers is unconditional. The costs of this care, however, are real and immediate. It costs over £1m a year just to keep the doors open. Our staff and carers provide the support that the terminally ill children and their families need, but they need the financial support necessary for Francis House to continue its work and for that we depend on you. We have received overwhelming support in the last 10 years for which we are eternally grateful. If we are to continue our work, that support needs to continue. Please remember, even the smallest sacrifice can change a life.'

CHAPTER 5

FUNDRAISING ORIGINS AND SUPPORTERS

Offers of help poured in once word was out that the north-west was getting its first children's hospice. The list of fundraisers was endless ... schools, churches, pubs, clubs, societies, solicitors, banks, building societies, freemasons, scouts, guides and dance schools.

Graham Cocking presents Sister Aloysius with a donation on behalf of the George Wimpey Charitable Trust

Fundraising Origins

The sporting world was equally generous ... golf, football, darts, snooker, swimming and bowls clubs all made similar goodwill gestures by generating much-needed funds. An army of fundraisers and volunteers was on the march. The fuse had been lit.

The care of children with life-limiting illnesses clearly touched a nerve within the community. The British public are renowned for their amazing generosity during times of

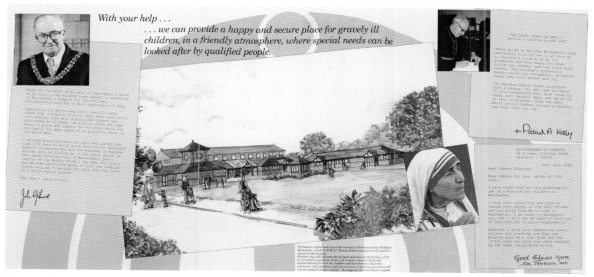

The Lord Mayor's brochure highlighting the need for a children's hospice in Manchester

great crisis. They had decided the call to action from Francis House was a deserving cause. Kids come first. That was the catalyst and the charity was so grateful its request for assistance was being met so emphatically.

A schoolboy even turned up at the hospice to hand over his pocket money, the coins wrapped up in scrap paper. Every little helps and fundraising was close to the magical £1m mark when the hospice opened at the start of November 1991. News of a children's hospice had been greeted warmly within the north-west and far beyond. Funnily enough, the first anonymous donation came from Spain, of all places.

Closer to home, the first declaration of support was received from the Lord Mayor of Manchester, Cllr John Gilmore. More than a year before Francis House opened, the civic leader got the ball rolling with a high-profile campaign to raise vital funds. The Mayor nominated Rainbow Family Trust as his chosen charity for his year of office, raising £58,000. He combined the appeal launch with an emotional plea for help, saying:

> 'Terminally ill adults and their families have, thank God, a hospice in which they can face their entry into eternal life with dignity and respect and are surrounded by kindness. We wish to offer the same haven of peace and support to the young child and its family for whom there is no provision here in the north-west.

> 'In this great bustling City of Manchester, proud capital of the North, could I ask that for just a few seconds within the quiet of your own mind you listen with me. I am sure you will hear the voice of a child saying ... please. The rest I leave to you.'

The Lord Mayor also published a promotional leaflet detailing the purpose of the hospice:

- To provide a happy and secure place for gravely ill children, in a friendly atmosphere, where special needs can be looked after by qualified people.
- To give parents and their other children an essential break from the strain of total, unremitting care.
- To offer friendship, encouragement and relief, enabling the whole family to return home refreshed.
- To provide a service to suit the family through counselling, homecare, day care, overnight stays and drop-in facilities.
- To provide a lifeline by being available day or night in any emergency.

The Lord Mayor's Ball on Saturday, 20 April 1991 took the hospice story into the heart of the Manchester business community. Bernard Lawson, from the Lord Mayor's office, was a tireless worker reviving the Ball which had once been a regular event in the social calendar. The gala event, hosted by celebrity couple Richard Madeley and Judy Finnigan, was the hottest ticket in town. Guests flocked to the Piccadilly Hotel in the city centre.

The Ball was sponsored by Manchester Airport and raffle prizes included flights to far-flung destinations readily donated by major airlines. Volunteers Moira Rossiter and Vera Kennedy were instrumental in making the event an overwhelming success. That was typical of two women who became phenomenal fundraisers for Francis House.

Fundraisers Vera Kennedy (left) and Moira Rossiter (right) with TV golden couple Richard Madeley and Judy Finnigan

Dancing the night away in aid of Francis House

I remember Sister Aloysius opening the post and dozens of letters of help from people keen to get on board.'

Moira set to work organising a successful fundraising committee of Cheshire ladies, who called on their long list of contacts for support. 'Moira was great fun and kick-started the fundraising with hard work and drive. She was a determined lady who got things done and brought in a lot of money, undoubtedly raising the profile of the hospice,' added Shaunagh.

Vera Kennedy was the wife of John Kennedy CBE, the founder of John Kennedy Civil Engineering and a generous supporter of charitable causes. Vera worked energetically behind the scenes organising ladies' lunches, fashion shows and golf events. One of the committee members was Brenda Bouker (née Winstanley). She worked for Moira's husband, Bill, as a bookkeeper at 1st National Locksmiths in Portland Street, Manchester.

Brenda said: 'We had so many donations from wonderful people wanting to help. Vera spent long hours on the phone asking people to buy raffle tickets and Moira was out three nights a week fundraising. The generosity was fantastic. It was an incredible time.' Moira also helped to set up the hospice visit by Diana, Princess of Wales, presenting her with two Rainbow Family Trust jumpers for her sons, Prince William and Prince Harry.

The two friends led the first fundraising group, known as Friends of Rainbow, which undeniably helped put Francis House on the map. Over a three-year period, Moira and Vera and their supporters helped raise more than £250,000, an incredible achievement. Such was their enormous contribution and the outpouring of love in those early years for a much-loved charity.

Shaunagh Carroll (née Ward) was the first employee of the charity, working from the garage on site with Francis House founder Sister Aloysius and Sister Austin. Shaunagh recalled: 'As word got out in the local communities that there were children in need of a hospice it was like lighting a fuse.

Sister Nicola Haarhuis abseiling down Manchester Town Hall

Moira and Vera even abseiled Manchester Town Hall to raise money and were joined on the adventure by Sister Nicola Haarhuis, who ran Mount Carmel respite home. The story of a Sister descending one of the city's tallest buildings featured in the *Manchester Evening News*. 'Nun but the Brave' read the newspaper's headline. 'I've never tried anything like this before. I must admit I've said a few extra prayers this morning,' said a nervous Sister Nicola.

Friends of Rainbow set up a charity shop on School Lane, Didsbury, which became a hive of activity. Use of the property, which was once an estate agent, was given rent-free by Seddon Developments until it was required by them. That could be weeks or months. It ended up being five years. In no time

Moira Rossiter presents Princess Diana with a Francis House sweater. The royal visit raised the profile of the fundraising appeals

at all, the Didsbury community knew there were bargains to be had at the shop which provided a steady stream of income.

A band of volunteers helped manager Moira Mulheran sell clothes, many of which were Marks & Spencer seconds. Games, toys and cards were donated and raised funds. Even after leaving the premises, Moira continued her roadshow, taking goods to nursing homes, hospitals and work canteens as long as she could.

Another fundraising group, allegedly of senior years, were formed, calling themselves The Golden Girls. Meanwhile, a Friends in a Million initiative was seen as a way of reaching the wider public. The ambitious plan was for a million people to donate £1 a year, a sum that might also attract children and the elderly.

Raising the profile was critical to maintain financial support. That meant gaining as much publicity as possible. Well-known television and radio personality Eamonn O'Neal used his extensive media contacts to offer support. The charity was close to his heart as his family had close local links with the Catholic Church. Other celebrities came forward. Former pop singer turned disc jockey Susie Mathis would spearhead the Kirsty Howard Appeal a decade after the hospice opened, while the cast of *Coronation Street* played their part in promoting Francis House.

●●●

The flurry of activity on the fundraising front was welcome news for Bernard Nagle. By the time he started his role as fundraising manager in July 1991 the fledgling charity was inundated with offers of goodwill and cash. A fundraising office was established in classrooms at St John Vianney School, in Stretford.

The first public fundraising concert took place in the convent grounds on Wednesday, 14 August 1990. It was attended by Father Francis, a popular Franciscan priest who enjoyed a large following across the diocese. Even by this early stage – some 15 months before opening – word was getting out that a new children's hospice was planned.

Kind-hearted local firms and organisations offered assistance. Support came from biscuit factory McVitie's, based in Levenshulme, Alexandra Hospital in Cheadle and British Aerospace. British Gas funded the entire boiler house requirements, including the heating system.

Kellogg's, with its giant factory in Trafford Park, pledged £10,000 over four years. Sharp promised to supply televisions and hi-fi systems, while lighting was provided free of charge. DIY store B&Q donated all the plants and shrubs, which turned up on two lorries. Successful applications for funds were made to the BBC Children in Need Appeal and the ITV Telethon Appeal. The BBC donated £200,000 and ITV awarded £25,000. Many other avenues of fundraising were pursued during these months. The sum of £25,000 came from Monica Byrne, of Mancunia Travel, to mark a quarter of a century of Mancunia travel pilgrimages.

An early public event in March 1991 was a concert by Siamsa Tire, an Irish folk dance group, at the Free Trade Hall. By the end of the following month total donations stood at £285,000, still well below the amount needed, especially with building costs rising to more than £1m and revenue costs rapidly approaching. The urgency was heightened by the fact children and families were anxiously waiting in the wings, desperately needing respite help.

Manchester's two football clubs, United and City, would arrive on the scene in due course, teaming up with Francis House for various activities. Supporters rallied to the cause, realising the value of the hospice. The local parish of St. Catherine's and its social club began raising funds at an early stage and continued a long association with the charity.

Kate Puć

From dancing with Sir Alex Ferguson to attending a ladies' darts presentation in Gorton ... it's all in a day's work for Kate Puć. There has never been a dull moment for Francis House's longest-serving fundraiser, who clocked up 28 years of service in October 2023.

Even her job interview was eventful, as she explained: 'I came here for a position as office manager and when Sister Aloysius realised I'd worked in sales, she thought I'd be better on the fundraising side because of my sales background.' Her first boss was Fundraising Director Bernard Nagle who had been with the charity from the early days.

Also part of their team was Shaunagh Carroll, who worked as a secretary for Sister Aloysius before moving to fundraising. Kate said: 'We started our fundraising from St John Vianney School in Stretford working from classrooms. We were all spread out with a classroom each. The charity also had the Rainbow Family Trust shop in the centre of Didsbury.

Kate Puć (front centre) joins Coronation Street stars to celebrate the hospice's 18th birthday

A photo-call with fundraisers at Sainsbury's in Stockport

'Bernard was an easy-going boss. Francis House was fresh in minds and people wanted to fundraise for us. We'd take phone calls from supporters who wanted to put on events. We ran various campaigns and we all helped out at concerts at Arley Hall. We got involved in everything that was going on and went along to offer support.'

Kate married husband Adam in May 1996 and their daughter Aniela was born two years later. Kate worked part-time until Aniela reached school age. 'It was the perfect job for me. I could be there raising my daughter, while doing the job I loved.

'Sister Aloysius was very family-oriented, but knew I was the type of person who would always give back. She was lenient with me and I'd do stuff from home so it was swings and roundabouts really. I've been a general fundraiser who has adapted to different places. A lot has changed. We went from a classroom in Stretford to a prefab at a school in Didsbury that was falling apart and freezing in winter and boiling hot in summer.

'We then spent ages on an industrial estate on Battersea Road in Heaton Mersey until the fundraising offices moved here to Francis House. It's been an amazing job and I've met so many people from different walks of life. One minute I'd be at a Gorton ladies' darts team presentation night and the next at Sir Alex Ferguson's golf and gala dinner at Mere where I got to dance with him. It's been that diverse.

'I've known some fundraisers for a long time and they're just nice people, so I've been very fortunate. A lot of my job involves obviously going out and about, whether it's giving talks to primary schools, high schools, women's groups or attending a golf day. We'll give support to anyone who needs it. It's such a varied job.'

Kate has a host of memories, including two Guinness world records. Lloyds Hotel Bowling Club, in Chorlton, set a record of 105 continuous hours of crown green bowls only to see their total beaten by Australian bowlers in beautiful weather. Undaunted, the Lloyds members regained the record by playing non-stop for 168 hours – almost a week – at South West Manchester Cricket Club.

Kate said: 'It was mid October and they played through rain, hail and ice. Conditions were dreadful. Some players cried and broke down, suffering from sleep deprivation. On the last day they were exhausted and as I walked round there was a rainbow over the bowling green. I'll always be grateful to them, in particular one of their members, Steve Ridley, who organised these events.

'We had another Guinness world record when Nick Rose, from Midshire Business Systems, organised a 72-hour football tournament which raised £45,000. I've kept in touch with a lot of our supporters, including Tim Grogan, from Deloitte, who've been fabulous supporters over the years. Ged Mason, owner of the Morson Group, raised £50,000 for us in 2018, keeping a promise that he would raise funds for Francis House.'

The Kirsty Howard Appeal had a massive effect on the fundraising team, much to Kate's delight. 'It brought Francis House to everyone's attention, both here and abroad. The phone would never stop ringing. The fundraising side just went up – it was incredible. Although many people thought they were fundraising for Kirsty, they were detached from the fact that she was a child who did come to Francis House.

'We would get stupid phone calls asking if David Beckham could go to my son's tea party. I think that was probably one of the busiest times in fundraising and it certainly raised awareness of the charity. So many events came out of that. Today, it's a different ball game. We have to go out to people and say can you fundraise for us. It's literally a case of trying to get people to do things.

'Yes, people do still want to fundraise for children, but around here you have an awful lot of charities for youngsters. We're not exactly fighting, but everyone is after that same penny. Sometimes days are so quiet because the phone hasn't rung. Francis House was new and fashionable at one time, but now there are so many children's causes. Yet costs don't go down. They go up and, as the cost of living is going up anyway, we need to bring in funds to keep the doors open.

'It's a Herculean task at the moment with only three of us trying to do that. I don't think we've completely recovered from Covid. People are still very wary of what's happening and aware of their financial situation. Understandably, people are more choosy about what they go to. They may have attended three events a year in the past but may now only go to one. I'm afraid its just a sign of the times.'

Hitting the heights … fundraiser Kate Puć with former Manchester United star David May on a trek to Machu Picchu

Kate trekked to Machu Picchu in Peru in 2011, raising £10,000 for the hospice. Former Manchester United defender David May joined her on the nine-day adventure as part of support by Manchester United Foundation, a charity partner at the time.

David Woodrow

Tall, handsome and eloquent... David Woodrow was a perfect front man for Francis House. His unmistakable smooth South African accent tempted thousands of supporters to dig deep into their pockets in aid of the hospice. David was always willing to present the case for Francis House, anywhere, anytime and before any audience. All he did was tell those listening intently about the everyday challenges facing the charity trying to make ends meet as it provided care for children and young adults with life-limiting illnesses. David's persuasive powers invariably worked. A consummate professional and a gentleman, his natural presentational skills had been honed in the classroom during nearly 40 years as a teacher.

He became fundraising manager at Francis House and stayed there for 15 years until his retirement in 2015 before continuing in a voluntary capacity. He became involved initially as a volunteer while he was deputy head teacher at The Ryleys School, in Alderley Edge. David had started his teaching career in Rhodesia, his birthplace, in 1940. He left his beloved homeland in 1980 due to political unrest.

Close friends Millie and Wyn Llewellyn organised a charity dinner at The Vicarage pub near their home in Holmes Chapel. David recalled:

'Sister Austin, from Francis House, was invited to speak at the event. Wow, what an inspiration. She was a fabulous, lovely lady and I couldn't help getting involved in some way raising funds for the hospice. We then held a charity ball, open days and raffles and one thing led to another.'

David's contacts book filled up once he started running the fundraising office as manager. He said: 'I loved the job. I loved going out talking to people and helping out at various functions and that sort of thing. I had retired from teaching when I came here full time and life was about to begin.

'At that stage Manchester United took us on in a massive way and we became one of the chosen charities for their Foundation. We had bucket collections outside Old Trafford at home games and we did abseils and zip wires into the stadium from the stands. Players came into the hospice bearing gifts for the

Manchester United's big signing ... Francis House was a chosen charity for the club's Foundation. Hospice fundraising manager David Woodrow is seen with the Manchester United players in 2010

United and England star Rio Ferdinand gets in some training on a computer game with Patrick at Francis House

and balls organised by Judy Bailey and her Cheshire ladies over many years. The money they raised was phenomenal and fortunately I was also involved. Renee and Mike Davey ran the silent auction at the ball. They were unbelievable evenings, attracting huge crowds. I remember we had a stall at a golf expo exhibition by the Trafford Centre, while the late Maurice Ireland organised sponsored walks around the Cheshire Three Peaks.'

children at Christmas and we had use of the pitch for a tournament.

'There was a Santa fun run around the ground and we were also allowed to use the training facility at Carrington for a seven-a-side football tournament. We were given signed shirts which we had framed, and footballs and boots to auction. Wendy Rennison, Gerrie McKiernan, John Shiels and Martin Feast were great helpers at United.

'The football shirts were framed by June Schofield, from ArtKo, and she saved us hundreds of pounds. Her son Michael was manager of Nando's restaurant across the road from the hospice. I got to know him well and he started all sorts of fundraising events for us. Ann Billington then appeared on the scene and involved Francis House as the beneficiary of the Irish Abroad dinner dance at the Hilton Hotel in Manchester. These dinners raised an awful lot of money for us, as did the concerts

Fundraising took all forms as supporters came up with creative ways to help. Pilot John Vincent flew his Britannia Airways jet on day trips to cities like Prague, Venice and Vienna. Planeloads of supporters bought raffle tickets from air hostesses who gave their time free of charge and served coffee and tea. An auction was held on the return flight.

Golf days always went with a swing with club members at Davyhulme Park and Stockport rallying to the cause. The late Jim Cash, whose son used Francis House, set up a long-standing annual competition at Stockport. Likewise, David Marsden at Davyhulme Park whose support team includes the tireless Nigel Richmond. The Devaney family also gave their support at their course in Holmes Chapel. A stalwart of the golfing

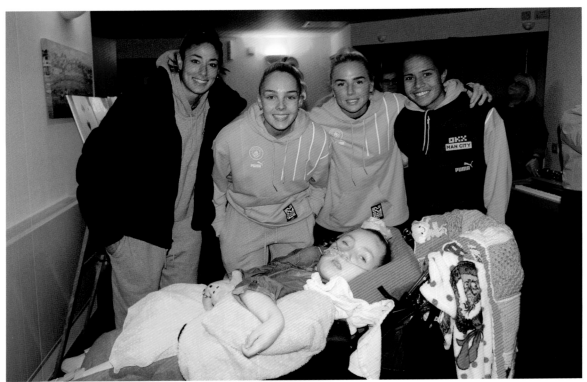

Manchester City players Leila Ouahabi, Ellie Roebuck, Alex Greenwood and Mary Fowler with Tehyah Solan-Clarke

scene was volunteer John Andrew, who raised thousands of pounds organising tournaments across dozens of countries, including Spain, Turkey, South Africa and Barbados.

Manchester City teamed up with the hospice, holding bucket collections outside the ground, providing shirts and footballs and holding a knockout tournament at their Academy. The list of supporters is endless. The Trafford Centre held an abseil, while the Wilmslow half marathon was also in aid of the charity. One of the most touching moments each Christmas came when a group of bikers went into the hospice bearing gifts and cash. The motorcyclists now visit the charity's outlet in the Quayside MediaCityUK, formerly the Lowry Outlet Mall.

The shopping complex has been the focal point for the charity's Festival of Christmas Trees, which raised an impressive £25,000 in 2022. The ingenious scheme has been running for 16 years with David helping in a voluntary capacity since relinquishing his role at the hospice in 2015. It was his idea and each year the retail outlet kindly lends the hospice a unit which is transformed into a winter wonderland. Companies and celebrities decorate trees and place gifts or vouchers at the base. The highest bid over a six-week period wins the goodies on offer.

David: 'I was in a shopping mall in Johannesburg while on holiday and was attracted by a large number of trees. I thought it was a wonderful idea and it has gone fantastically well. Fundraising officer Julie Williams has done a great job, taking it online and that's resulted in the festival generating a lot more money.'

Famous artist the late Harold Riley was strolling near his Salford home when he ended up getting involved. 'We were still in the middle of decorating the trees when Harold Riley stood there looking at them. Normally, I'd suggest that someone comes back when it's finished but thank goodness I didn't. I explained what was going on and he said: "Do you have a spare tree?" I said: "Yes," even though I didn't know if we had.

'There's a photograph of him decorating a tree with cards he'd drawn. It was the first year we ran the event and his artwork helped raise a lot of money.'

David and wife Esther donated an Out of Africa tree, complete with handmade decorations they brought from South Africa.

One of David's greatest triumphs was persuading comedian Peter Kay to stage a special one-off show at Chester racecourse. The event raised a staggering £170,000. David recalled:

'Peter became quite a good buddy and we met every now and again at charity events he was either doing for us, or partly for us. He was appearing at the Piccadilly Hotel in Manchester and I spotted him on stage by himself while the raffle was taking place. I thought, I'm going to ask him if he'd do something especially for Francis House. He said he'd love to help and didn't want a fee. We had a marvellous night which I'll never forget.'

Artist Harold Riley with his portrait of Sister Aloysius

Jim Nicholas

Elvis impersonator Jim Nicholas confesses to a *Burning Love* for Francis House. He admits he is *All Shook Up*, having raised more than £200,000 for the hospice which, according to Jim, is *Always On My Mind*. While Presley was the King of Rock and Roll, Jim is the King of Fundraising.

The showman has been entertaining audiences with his Elvis act for over five decades. Every time Jim has strutted his stuff, he puts out a collection box, benefitting a charity close to his heart. Jim, a retired head gardener for the Bishop of Salford, said:

> *'When I first went to Francis House and saw the families, I felt I wanted to do everything I could for them. Without Francis House these families would be stuck. If I can help someone along the way and make people happy, I'm happy.'*

Jim, from Swinton, is a close friend of showbiz partner and comic Jimmy Cricket, another Francis House supporter. The pair were introduced by Sister Aloysius. Jim received a golden collection box from the charity to mark his amazing contribution.

Chief Executive David Ireland said: 'What Jim has achieved is phenomenal. He's shown incredible generosity and commitment to Francis House with his fundraising for more than 25 years and we can't thank him enough.'

Jim's talents do not end with Elvis. His Cliff Disco has seen him perform for the Cliff Richard fan club and he has also appeared on stage as Jimmy Osmond and Tina Turner. No wonder he's *Simply The Best*.

Mary and Alan Gillatt

Mary Gillatt never really knew what her job title was at Francis House – and didn't mind in the slightest! Mary spent 18 years there doing all sorts of jobs until she officially retired in 2018. She and husband Alan, who ran the hospice charity shop in Burnage for nine years, are still heavily involved with fundraising as volunteers.

It's a connection that goes back to the start. Mary was part of the charity committee at McVitie's biscuit factory in Levenshulme when the hospice was being built. Mary said: 'The hospice approached McVitie's, as one of the biggest employers, to do some fundraising for them and we agreed without hesitation. We'd organise things like It's A Knockout events, book sales and had a savings scheme in

Elvis impersonator Jim Nicholas and comedian Jimmy Cricket

Supporters Alan and Mary Gillatt are joined by David Woodrow

which Francis House received all the interest. We bought a minibus for them from that.

'I was on good terms with Sister Aloysius and Sister Austin and I was suddenly made redundant by McVitie's. Sister Aloysius found out and offered me a job. I got home and Alan asked me what I was going to be doing and I said I'd never asked her. I didn't know whether I was cleaning the toilets, reading to the kids, serving dinners or typing letters. I wasn't sure what I'd be doing but didn't care.

'It was Francis House and does it matter anyway what I'm doing as long as I'm being useful? At first, I didn't know what my job was and I sort of fumbled my way through almost 20 years of working there.

'I was like a jack of all trades to be honest. I was 'admin' or 'care team' and helped Pauline

Armitage in finance for 18 months and then moved to helping fundraising working alongside David Woodrow. Basically, I did anything that needed doing. I wouldn't put a title on my job at all.'

The couple have been involved in all kinds of fundraising activities as volunteers, including selling waterproof shower radios surplus from the Commonwealth Games in 2002 which had been donated to them.

Mary said: 'We sold them for £1 and made an average of £300 a week for the hospice until they were all gone. Francis House means everything to us. It's a privilege to be involved. I've said to people in the past that if you're minding someone's child it's the most precious thing they can let you do.

'If that child is able to tell you whether

it's hurting, or unhappy, or needs something, that's fine. But to allow someone else to take care of your child who can't communicate but still be confident they're being looked after in the same way that you'd look after them is beyond words.'

Tracey Sutherland

Mum Tracey Sutherland turned her passion for sewing into making face coverings as a thank you to Francis House, raising more than £800. Her family were supported by the charity for 14 years. Tracey and husband Steve lost son Daniel in 2011, aged 17. Twin brother Andrew and older brother Matthew were also helped by the hospice.

Tracey said: 'We took a lot of convincing to come to a children's hospice. We didn't accept that Dan's condition was life shortening and that no matter how poorly he got he would bounce back a few days later. The boys all had fantastic times at Francis House. They used to say we're going to his holiday home. We know that Francis House loved caring for him and this is our way of saying thank you.'

Tracey Sutherland sewing face coverings for Francis House

Chick Appeal

It was a crafty idea, but once it was hatched the chick appeal certainly spread its wings! No one chickens out of buying the cute woolly chicks and bunnies knitted by supporters every Easter. Each chick is filled with a donated chocolate egg and sold for £1 in schools, stores and businesses to raise funds for Francis House.

The Easter Chick Knit Appeal began more than 20 years ago, raising a record £74,000 in 2019. Its success is down to the handiwork of scores of talented knitters, crochet experts and Cadbury Creme Egg donors. Part-time care team volunteer Jackie Hadfield saw a vicar's wife knitting chicks for a church bazaar and developed the idea for Francis House.

Once her husband, John, a headteacher, took her chicks into schools, the Radcliffe couple discovered they were on to a winner. Jackie, a special needs teacher, said: 'The chickens were so popular with the children that I was knitting hundreds. I needed help so put out a call for people to either donate wool or get knitting. Kitchen and reception volunteers at Francis House were among those who came to my rescue.'

A group including Margaret Mayne, Mary Dooler and Glenda Fraser were making more than 550 chicks each year by 2012, while Costco Manchester and Tesco, at East Didsbury, donated creme eggs. Knitters even bought eggs, scouring supermarket shelves for discount offers.

Chick crazy ... knitters Margaret Mayne (left) and Mary Dooler show their handiwork

The following year saw the chick craze reach new heights after a media campaign by PR and Press Officer Karen Flower. Knitting magazines, crafting websites, local news outlets and hospice newsletter subscribers were all targeted by Karen. Requests for the pattern came from far and wide, including Italy, France, Spain and Australia.

News of the appeal even reached two remote villages in Uganda where around 80 women knitted 5,000 chicks over seven months. They were paid fairly for their endeavours by a kind-hearted benefactor in the UK. Margaret said: 'It's gone global! They've been arriving in all sizes and colours, although the pattern does say yellow wool. A few have had rather saggy bottoms, so the chocolate egg falls out. We've had to stitch

them up, but it's wonderful so many people have wanted to knit and support us.'

Fundraising officer Rachel Nasiri has supervised the appeal since 2015, developing its success. Rachel co-ordinates egg collectors, delivery drivers, school sellers and other volunteers known as 'stuffers' who help fill every single chick. More than 700 knitters and crocheters are involved in the project. Margaret Drury, from Monton, single-handedly knitted 1,205 chicks in 2019, while St Richard's Primary School, Longsight, collected 2,958 eggs and sold hundreds of chicks.

Select Transport, based at Manchester Airport, donated a delivery driver for two days to distribute more than 8,500 chicks to Urmston, Salford, Stockport and Oldham. The operation was scaled back during Covid,

Knitters in Uganda join in the Easter Chick Knit Appeal

though helpers refused to give up. Rita and Phil Andrew stuffed chicks tirelessly at their Northwich home, while Sarah Walker Sargent, from Bramhall, delivered and sold them from her car boot. Knitters Maria Dunbobbin, from Cheadle, and Sharon Wilkinson, from Gatley, skilfully created colourful and quirky chick combinations and repaired damaged beaks and wonky eyes in the chick hospital.

Despite the pandemic, the appeal raised a remarkable £30,000 and by 2022 it had bounced back with more than 32,000 chicks flying the nest from Francis House. Rachel said: 'From its beginnings as a chick knit by our hospice volunteers, and through the hard work of our supporters and the wider knitting community, the Easter Chick Knit has become a much-loved annual appeal with

a fantastic feel-good factor. Every single chick knitted, and every egg donated, really makes a big difference to us.'

Treks

Trekkers Helen Gorton and June Allingan can vouch that the Accursed Mountains live up to their name. The intrepid Francis House fundraisers fell victim to the curse of the Albanian Alps in 2019, slipping on difficult terrain and hurting their ankles so badly they could not finish the trek.

As other walkers headed off across the Valbona pass, which links two glacial valleys and is only passable by foot, Helen and June embarked on a seven-hour taxi ride, the fastest route to the next guesthouse by road. The pair did beat the trekkers there – but only just! The curse struck again when the group missed their connecting flight home and were left stranded in Frankfurt for a day while nursing aching joints and heavy backpacks.

There have been five treks, with more than £156,000 raised. The next adventure is planned for the Pyrenees in 2024. The toughest assignment was to the Home of the Giants, Norway's highest mountain, in 2022. Walkers crossed a glacier and the first day's trek took 12 hours, twice as long as planned, due to a diversion.

Walkers with enough energy jogged the last section to the mountain cabin to beg the kitchen to stay open to avoid missing their evening meal. The expeditions started in 2013 with a desert trek to the ancient site of Petra, in Jordan. Participants floated in the Dead Sea and slept in Bedouin tents beneath the stars.

Two years later, Morocco featured the contrast of the freezing Atlas Mountains and the heat of Marrakesh. Then, in 2017, it was off to Iceland and a trek through the Land of Fire and Ice. Walkers navigated glaciers, coastal inlets and fjords, a landscape constantly changed by volcanic activity.

The oldest trekker Deacon Ken Holding, from Wigan, shows incredible stamina. He was 77 when he undertook the Norwegian challenge. Ken has been on every trek, as have David and Judith Ireland. Other regular trekkers include trustees Judith Amosi-Khodadad, Jane Kempler and Dr Andrew Taylor, an experienced member of Oldham mountain rescue team. He has acted as the trip doctor, tending to many a bump, graze, concussion and sprain. Gill Bevin, a former Director of Care, and her sister Jan went on every trek until her retirement in 2020.

Trekkers tackle the Albanian Alps

CHAPTER 6

KEY FIGURES

Thanks to the vision of Sister Aloysius, the lives of thousands of families from across the north-west were transformed. Her legacy lives on through the smiling faces of the beautiful children and young adults who call Francis House their second home.

Sister Aloysius FMSJ

It is no exaggeration to say that the hospice would not have been built without her indestructible spirit and leadership. Sister was a remarkable woman whose determination turned a vague idea into reality in record time.

Barely 18 months after the brave decision was made to build a children's hospice, Princess Diana officially opened Francis House. Rarely can a project have gone from drawing board to delivery at such breakneck speed. This amazing achievement was testimony to Sister's tenacity, faith and strength of purpose.

Yet once Sister Aloysius saw the need for a place of respite for sick children there was no stopping her. She was on a mission. Even when that mission was accomplished, and the hospice was open, the hard graft was only just beginning. From then on, the formidable task facing Sister Aloysius and her trusted team was to deliver the service it had promised.

That meant wrapping their loving arms around children with unimaginable serious illnesses and their fatigued families. Such genuine and instinctive warmth and affection was all part of the package of practical respite care to make family life slightly less of a burden.

With the inspirational Sister Aloysius at the helm, there was always a confidence and belief that Francis House would flourish. From the age of 15, Sister knew she wanted to consecrate her life to God. She entered the congregation of the Franciscan Missionaries of St. Joseph and made her first vows just before her 18th birthday in 1945.

In the 1950s she was appointed to Didsbury where the Sisters, working within the Catholic Children's Rescue Society, cared for more than 100 children in a large children's home on Parrswood Road. Sister Aloysius was responsible for reuniting children from the home with their own families where possible. After she set up a fostering department, the work of finding foster families increased enormously.

For 20 years of her life, Sister put her heart and soul into developing the provision for children in need of care in the Diocese of Salford. Her maxim was that 'good childcare is good family life.'

In 1975, Sister was elected Superior General of her congregation, a post she held for 12 years. She was responsible for the whole mission of the congregation in England, Ireland, Scotland, the Netherlands, Kenya, Malaysia, the Philippines and North and South America. She maintained her links with the Rescue Society and remained a member of the Rescue Council, rarely missing a monthly meeting.

In 1989, the Rescue Society's work had developed to provide respite care for children with disabilities with foster parents. It became apparent that a number of these children had a short life expectancy. Sister Aloysius was appointed to a small sub-committee to investigate the needs of such children and their families. The rest, as they say, is history ...

In July 1990, the Rainbow Family Trust was given charity status. Sister Aloysius was appointed as Company Secretary and Administrator. Her next mission was to raise awareness of the need for a children's hospice and bring in necessary funds to build the children's hospice. Time was of the essence, especially as she knew families who might soon suffer the loss of a loved one.

Her single-minded approach was important. Sister inspired many, from all

Sister Aloysius retires in 2005 with (from left) Monsignor Thomas Mulheran, Ged Cosgrove, the Archbishop of Liverpool Patrick Kelly, David Ireland and Robin Wood CBE

walks of life, to support Francis House, a charity recognised and respected thanks to her unstinting work. Sister retired as Chief Executive in 2005, aged 78, but remained actively involved until ill-health took its toll.

Right to the end she was interested in all the new developments planned for Francis House and the provision of age-appropriate care for the adolescents and young people there. Sister Aloysius died on 29 August 2012 in Nazareth House, Prestwich. She was 85.

Her death came 24 hours before Sir Alex Ferguson laid the foundation stone for the Francis Lodge extension. She may have gone, but she was not forgotten. Her legacy was immeasurable. The new seven-bedroom complex opened in 2014, equipped with the latest technology in PlayStations, televisions and self-lowering wash basins. The Lodge also boasted a recording studio, cinema room, first-floor terrace and gardens. Sister Aloysius touched many lives. Here are a few tributes...

Co-founder Monsignor Thomas Mulheran:

'Sister Aloysius had tremendous grit, an iron will, and focus. She was a woman of outstanding faith and if she hadn't been a Sister, she'd have been top of her profession. She was the most loyal, supportive person and if she was behind you, things were going to go right. She was the sort of person who told you what she thought and didn't miss a thing. But everything was for the benefit of the children and their families.'

Chair of Trustees the late Robin Wood CBE:

'She was a lady of great determination who, once assured of the pressing need in the Manchester area pursued that goal with such speed it was achieved within 18 months.'

Former Manchester United manager Sir Alex Ferguson:

'Anyone who met Sister Aloysius will know what a truly lovely lady she was. Her amazing dedication to help terminally ill children and their families through very difficult times will never be forgotten.'

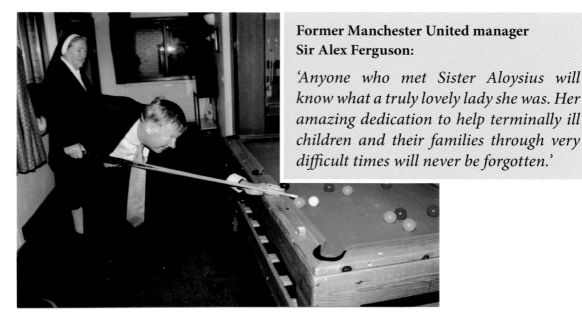

Former Clinical Lead Natalie Hands:

'I only ever experienced kindness from Sister Aloysius. She was compassionate but could come across as quite severe and had a wicked sense of humour. She didn't suffer fools gladly. I remember walking down the drive at Francis House after making a home visit with a colleague. Sister was coming the other way and said: 'One of you is keeping bad company, but I can't decide which one.' She had an air of authority about her. I never experienced it myself, but you wouldn't want to cross her, probably because she looked severe. She made an incredible contribution to Francis House.'

Sister Maureen FMSJ: 'Sister Aloysius was a woman of prayer and faith. When we were novices, she talked to us about learning to spend time in prayer. She came back to the offices of the Catholic Children's Rescue Society after being head of the Franciscan Missionaries of St Joseph. As Superior General, it was a big job with lots of travelling which she did for 12 years, opening and closing houses and missions. She would say: "Sister, I have a little job for you. It's in Peru and you leave next week." When she retired, she came to Mass every day in a wheelchair pushed by Sister Austin. Sister Aloysius was especially good with visits to the sick Sisters.'

Trustee Martin Lochery:

'Sister Aloysius was a force of nature. I recall one of our supporters, Eamonn O'Neal, saying to me about her: "Once Sister Aloysius asks you to do something, you stand up, do what she says and you do it smiling." That was the power of the woman. I mean, she was amazing. She worked like nobody's business. She spent her time making sure all the connections she needed were the right connections. She gave everything to this place.'

Speed was key for Sister Aloysius getting Francis House built

Former Head of Care Margaret Hickie:

'Sister Aloysius was very dynamic and extremely supportive of me. I was interviewed by her and Father Tom for my job and they were lovely people. There were quite a few people around the table as well that day for my interview.'

Sister Philomena FMSJ:

'Sister Aloysius was very strict and had a high expectation of the Sisters within Rescue and those working with Francis House. In the 1940s and 1950s, convents weren't seen as professionally trained so as a voluntary group we had to work hard to be accepted as an adoption and fostering agency. Sister Aloysius encouraged us to raise our profile to show we did actually have that professional level of expertise and we could work more or less as an equal partnership with local authorities.'

Sister Joan FMSJ:

'Sister Aloysius was the main person who recognised the need initially for respite care for children with disabilities. Families with children at home were so exhausted and needed respite. Sister was a force to be reckoned with. If you were in any spot of bother, she would be there for you and support you.'

Volunteer Pauline Armitage MBE:

'Sister Aloysius was totally devoted to the job. She had no time for any side issues. She was extremely supportive of her staff but if you did something she didn't like, she'd tell you. She was very straightforward but she had charisma.'

Monsignor Thomas Mulheran

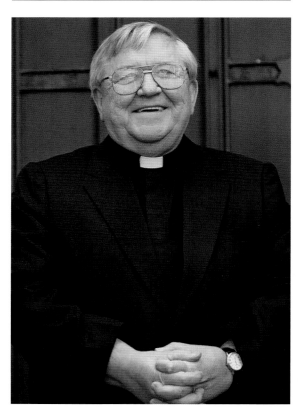

Monsignor Thomas Mulheran was the father figure at Francis House in every respect. This unassuming, humble, charismatic priest was co-founder, chaplain and trustee of the hospice. The tributes which poured in when he passed away in September 2022, aged 83, showed the enormous respect for a man who literally was a Godsend.

Through his impressive intellect, deep spirituality and caring pragmatism he helped thousands of families cope during very difficult times. His role in the history of this unique hospice will never be forgotten. The Monsignor's guiding hand saw the convent converted into a hospice within the space of 18 months.

He did actually have influence in high places, a crucial factor in creating the hospice. Father Tom, as everyone called him, was hugely respected within the Diocese of Salford and used his persuasive powers to secure the funding for the ambitious project.

One of his greatest gifts was the ability to deliver a homily that touched the hearts of believers and non-believers. Born in Rochdale in November 1938, he was ordained to the priesthood in June 1963. In 1971, he began his work with the Catholic Children's Rescue Society and became its secretary. He was also the financial secretary of Salford R.C. Diocese and a trustee.

Father Tom shared the same vision as Sister Aloysius as they embarked on their special project to build the hospice. Father Tom was loved by all who went to Francis House. Children, families, staff and volunteers.

Here are a few reflections of a great man ...

Chief Executive Revd David Ireland:

'Francis House and the families who use it owe so much to the far sightedness of Father Tom. He made it financially possible, and many families have benefitted personally from his priestly ministry as our chaplain, but he did so much more.'

Sister Aloysius and Father Tom in Kenya in 1982

Former Head of Care Margaret Hickie:

'Father Tom was a lovely person and the families loved him. He wouldn't be here all the time but came if we needed him. The families got to know him and he would say Mass every week in the chapel for the Sisters.'

Sister Philomena FMSJ:

'They worked well together, didn't they? Father Tom was involved with the Rescue Council of the Catholic Children's Rescue Society so was instrumental in ensuring everything was in place for the hospice to be built. He secured the Council's permission to hand over the buildings.'

Accountant Ged Cosgrove:

'Father Tom, Sister Aloysius and Sister Austin were like The Three Musketeers really. They built the place and pushed it forward after realising there was a need for children with terminal illnesses. Father Tom was an intelligent man and knew a lot about finance. He'd been involved in various financial activities relating to the diocese, so was commercially aware.'

Father Tom at the blessing of the site for Francis Lodge

Volunteer Pauline Armitage MBE:

'Father Tom was the backbone of the hospice. He was totally supportive of Sister Aloysius in what she was aiming to do. He was a high-powered man in the church, so had the weight of the Diocese of Salford behind him.

'He shared the same philosophy as Sister Aloysius and was the sort of person who would always find time to talk to everyone of all faiths. The parents held him in high regard. He would come out in the middle of the night to help and support them and the children. Father Tom was just brilliant.'

Former Clinical Lead Natalie Hands:

'Father Tom and Sister Aloysius were a great combination and he always stopped to talk when we passed on the driveway at the hospice. Father was always prepared to listen and when we asked about starting a Memory Day, he said: "Let me think about it. If we do it, we want to do it right." He drove a fast car and let us use it to attend a bereavement counselling course in Sheffield twice a month. It had heated seats and he was concerned we'd be okay in it.

'If a parent didn't want God mentioned in a funeral service, Father Tom would mention love instead, on the basis that God is love. He was a warm, sensitive man and everything was 'marvellous' and 'fantastic.' He was a hands-off type of person and would only come to things if invited.'

Sister Maureen FMSJ:

'Father Tom was a rock of strength and gave wonderful homilies at Mass, always about the love of God. Before Francis House, Father Tom and Father O'Leary would drive a coach to Lourdes, Rome and Assisi. The Sisters would be on board. He always said yes to requests and was wonderful with bereaved families at funerals. He was so good to the Sisters in so many ways. Father Tom was from Rochdale, the same town as our Foundress and lost his mother when he was 16. He worked in a greengrocers and on a building site before seminary.'

Sister Austin FMSJ

Sister Austin dedicated her life to the children and families of Francis House. She worked tirelessly to help countless families and was always the voice of reason and moderation. Sister played a major role in the inception, building and smooth running of the hospice.

Unassuming and always content to be part of a team operating quietly in the background, she never sought praise or thanks. Sister Austin had a keen sense of humour and was a trusted and loyal friend to many. Another of her qualities was the respect she held for others. She was also non-judgemental.

Well known to thousands around the north-west, Sister lived out her deep faith as she followed her vocation to help those in greatest need. Sister Austin was first appointed by the Catholic Children's Rescue Society in 1963 where she held several demanding roles until 1991.

She was a social worker helping families in difficulties and later worked as a fostering officer. The anguish of the children she assisted deeply affected her. That only reinforced her determination to find foster families for them. She loved the teenage girls at West Bank Approved School, in Heaton Mersey, where she worked and believed in them resolutely. Her sense of humour really came to the fore at this time.

In 1991, Sister Austin started work at Francis House. Her many unsung roles included touring parishes to raise money for the building and spearheading many fundraising social events. She was a gracious guest at many functions, collecting cheques from generous donors and organising beautiful displays for memorial days and open days at the Hospice.

Sister Austin spent several years living with and caring for Sister Aloysius with whom she worked for many years. The pair were extremely close, sharing similar interests and memories of the development of the Rescue Society and the birth of Francis House. Together they documented a book about the history of Rescue, a valuable record which charted its fascinating progress helping those greatly in need.

Sister Austin remained a highly valued member of staff at Francis House until 2018 when ill-health forced her to retire, but she was still passionately interested in everything going on there. Sister Austin died at the

Franciscan Convent, Blackburn, in February 2019, aged 81.

Former Clinical Lead Natalie Hands:

'Sister Austin was a real sweetie and was from the north-east. I remember as I waited for my job interview at Francis House, she took a tray of drinks in for the interview panel and came and sat next to me, putting me totally at ease. She was always interested in my family and remembered different things I had said. When my daughter got married, she said "I want to see the pictures". She was very personable, easy to talk to and very thoughtful.

'On Memory Days she would always decorate the chapel with beautiful flowers and ornaments. She was quite artistic in that way. She always did something special for families. She would put a verse or a saying with a bag, a candle or a special flower. She did all that herself.'

Accountant Ged Cosgrove:

'Sister Austin just seemed to do everything and would get on with things. Initially, she did the wages and was like a No 2 and would always make things happen.'

From left, Sisters Francine, Austin and Maureen during the building of Francis Lodge

Chief Executive Revd David Ireland:

'Sister Austin worked quietly behind the scenes right up until she became ill with cancer. She was such an important figure in the history of the hospice and always there in the background. She performed many different roles, including typing up newsletters at the very beginning.'

Volunteer Pauline Armitage MBE:

'Sister Austin hid her light under a bushel and was very involved in the practical work, making sure things got done. She was easy to work for. She knew what she wanted and what had to be done. She would never ask someone to do something she wouldn't do herself.'

Sister Maureen FMSJ:

'Sister Austin supported Sister Aloysius every step of the way. She had great wisdom and experience and had been a Sister in charge at Rescue. She was practical and good with computers and designing Service sheets. She was also involved with the finance and salaries at Francis House. She also gave talks to various groups. Thoughtful and kind, Sister Austin was always smiling.'

Senior care team member Jackie Graham:

'Sister Austin was lovely. She had an amazing sense of humour and was just an incredible person. She was very driven and focused and knew exactly what was going on.'

Revd David Ireland

As a former architect, Revd David Ireland has always had grand designs for Francis House. That is because he only wants the best for the children, young adults and their families who use the hospice. He has a heart of gold, a common denominator among all the staff and volunteers who bring smiles where often there is sadness.

Everyone cares passionately, no one more than David. The chief executive leads by example. Every decision is made with the welfare of the family at heart, true to the founding principles of Francis House. David

The Catholic Children's Rescue Society offices are demolished in 2012 to make way for Francis Lodge

knows the story of almost every youngster who has visited the hospice in more than three decades.

As a church minister, he has conducted quite a few of their funerals. Such is the nature of life and death at a place families regard as a haven of warmth and compassion. David created Francis House, quite literally, in his role as architect for the project to turn a convent into a hospice in 1990.

He already knew the site intimately. Four years earlier he had designed an extra storey for offices of the Catholic Children's Rescue Society located next door. Salford R.C. Diocese liked his work and a friendship was formed with Rescue Secretary Father Thomas Mulheran.

David said: 'For them to give a 33-year-old this job was putting a lot of trust in me. It would have been more difficult to build if

it hadn't been for Martin House. They were desperate for us to open as they had to stop taking children from outside their area. Father Tom, Sister Aloysius and myself went over there.

'Their Administrator Robin Wood told us later he knew the hospice was going to happen. He said he'd never seen a hospice go from inception to opening in such a short time and it would never happen again. A lot of the things we did were based on the Martin House model. But instead of being given a four-acre field to build a new hospice on, I was given this 1950s convent.

'It was a real test. Not only from the point of view of providing something that was right for the families at the time and complied with legislation, but to do something that was architecturally acceptable with an old 1950s building within a tight budget because they had no money. So, it was a difficult challenge. It was a real privilege to be able to do it. I must say we made a massive loss as an architectural practice, because I just put so much of my own time into it. It was a life chance.'

David fell in love with Francis House and formally became a trustee in July 1994. Legal requirements meant he had to wait until his firm Hulme Upright were no longer receiving fees from the charity.

'Meeting Father Tom and Sister Aloysius changed my life. When I first walked through the gates in 1986, I was told by my senior partner not to spend any time here because there was no money in it and I'm still here.

It was odd to be asked to design a building that would be opened by royalty, the first of its kind in the north-west. My colleagues at work made fun of me when a headline in the local newspaper said, "The Architect."

'I became good friends with Robin and Lenore Hill at Martin House and didn't want to put this behind me and go on to something else. That's why I became a trustee adviser initially, helping with building inspections and so on. Once I became a trustee in 1994, I joined the fundraising and finance committees which were basically the same group of people.

'The financial situation of the hospice was precarious at the time. We were concerned we

Sister Aloysius and David Ireland

might go the way of other children's hospices and just fade away, or have to be taken over by health authorities. All the time I felt I was being called to ministry in the church and after seven years training to be an architect (qualifying in 1982) I then went to theological college in 1992 and was ordained in 1995. I became the Minister at the United Reformed Church in the centre of Oldham. They asked me to be there for a year while they sorted themselves out and I'm still there now.'

David ran the Manchester office at the expanding architectural firm. A major client was Shrewsbury Diocese. If the church had been calling a decade earlier, Francis House was calling when Sister Aloysius retired and David replaced her in 2005.

David said: 'I couldn't believe it when they asked me to apply for the job as chief executive. The post was advertised externally. There were five candidates. Four were interviewed and I was offered the post. It wasn't something I was looking for. I thought I was going to be on the selection committee.

'It changed my life completely. I loved being an architect, but I felt a real passion for what we were doing here. I can't believe I've been in this position and able to do the great things we've done. It's not an easy thing to be a minister and a chief executive. Being seen as the go-to person. Staff come to me with their problems; families come to me with their problems. There are a lot of different issues presented to you.'

Father Tom conducted many of the funeral services in the early years. David fulfils that role now, if asked. The choice obviously rests with families, depending on their faith. 'I tend to be asked by families who've got to know us really well and who've been coming for respite,' said David.

He sees Francis House as one big team. 'We've always got to be proud of what Francis House does, but it's not one person. The clinical team does a brilliant job, but we couldn't do that if the maintenance team weren't backing them up and keeping everything going. The fundraisers bring in the money. Everyone comes together to contribute. The cleaning staff worked so hard to keep us all safe during Covid.

'That's the good thing about Francis House. No one is seen as better than anyone else. Everyone's skills are being used for the whole. We recognise everyone's importance, including volunteers. I've been lucky to work with only three registered managers, all of whom have been great at their job. Other hospices are constantly changing staff.

'We've been true to our founding principles and philosophy. Sister Aloysius, Father Tom and myself shared a similar liberal attitude with the hospice set up for people of all faiths and no faith. Everyone is treated equally, regardless of culture, religion or gender.'

The death of Father Tom in 2022 left a void. 'One person I really miss is Father Tom because we could always talk things through together and I haven't got that now. There is a feeling that of the original people, I'm the one left to turn the lights off. It feels a bit that way, but the hospice will carry on like a juggernaut.

'It will change and other people will take over, but I've been lucky to have been in charge at a time when we were able to expand and develop the service to meet the ever-increasing need. To be honest, I'm not sure we'll be able to meet the need in the future because the numbers are increasing all the time. We've got more people coming to us, but they're living longer which is a good thing.

'I always thought we should have a third residential unit before I retired, but I'm not going to be able to do that now. Covid got in the way unfortunately.'

Here's what others have to say about David's contribution…

Trustee Martin Lochery:

'I knew David when he was an architect, through his work with schools, and he had the reputation of being very straight and he delivered. There were a lot of architects who didn't get comments like that. David is from the same mould as Sister Aloysius. He's honest and very hard working. He knows exactly what he wants and he makes sure he has the right people around him in order to deliver the right thing. He's so totally committed to here.'

Chair of Trustees Chris Roberts:

'David's contribution to Francis House has been immense. If David asks us to do things on behalf of the hospice, we do them. He played an enormous role in the development of Francis Lodge and the residential units. He's always on call and will turn out in the early hours if necessary. His ethos is Francis House, the young people and their families and he cares very deeply about it.'

Accountant Ged Cosgrove:

'I don't think you could put the health of the hospice in better hands. He lives and breathes it. He can come over as quite strict and "ruling the roost" a little bit, but you couldn't have anyone better in that role. He's a top man and his heart and soul is in it. I trust him wholeheartedly with everything. He wouldn't do anything for himself, it's all about the hospice.'

Volunteer Pauline Armitage MBE:

'David has driven all the progress to develop the hospice. He's done all that and while the hospice may be a different place, the philosophy hasn't changed. Nothing stands still with David. He's always looking for the next thing and that's right. That's how it should be.'

Sister Philomena FMSJ:

'David has done an excellent job over many years. Sister Aloysius and Father Tom had that vision and while the buildings may have changed over time, the principles have remained unchanged from the day we left the convent to make way for the hospice.'

Former Clinical Lead Natalie Hands:

'If you cut David down the middle, he would have Francis House written all the way down like Blackpool rock. He has a vision and it's great to have someone like that who sticks to it. If someone wanted to do things differently, he'd have clear reasons if he didn't feel it was a good idea. I appreciated that because you knew where you were and where you stood.

'You rarely saw Sister Aloysius who was in her office and didn't go in for lunch, whereas David got to know people. He's very kind. My car was stolen once when I had to park it outside. David immediately got me a Francis House car so I could get home that night. He sorted out all the insurance and did it without me even asking. How many bosses do that? He's very compassionate and caring, but with a firmness. You can't hoodwink him or take him for a ride. He can see through people.'

Judith Ireland with husband David on site as Francis Lodge takes shape

CHAPTER 7

FIRST CLASS CARE

The number of families on the roll at Francis House exceeded 500 for the first time in 2018. Of that total, about 350 children and young adults were using the hospice for respite care. Add parents and siblings and it meant the charity was supporting more than 2,000 people through its various services.

The Care Numbers

The enlarged Francis House family did, however, highlight the need for more money to fund additional care requirements. By early 2023, the number of youngsters receiving some form of help had risen to 573, of which 400 had respite care. The other 173 families were accessing other types of support, including bereavement, psychotherapy, emotional, homecare and legal advice.

In total, the number of families who have used Francis House since records began is 1,537. Throughout the charity's history, trustees have refused to accept contracts from the government for respite care.

Chief Executive David Ireland explained: 'If we accepted contracts for Statutory services then we would be using charity money to provide cheap provision for the NHS. As

Statutory provision is limited anyway, we prefer to provide additional support for the families using charitable sources. We always allocate beds on a greatest need basis, rather than reserve them for local authorities.'

Francis House keeps administrative costs as low as possible, hence 91.78p of every pound donated in 2022 went directly towards care. That figure of almost 92 per cent was much higher than many other charities. The administrative team is made up of Chief Executive David Ireland, Deputy Rachael Taylor and PA Karen Smail. The hospice has only one PR employee, Karen Flower, whereas other similar-sized charities might have up to seven staff in their Communications team.

Opposite page: All in a day at Francis House

Above: The recipe for happiness. Inaya and Faizan having fun and games in the kitchen

Opposite page: Special moments captured at Francis House

Margaret Hickie – Head of Care and Registered Manager 1991–2009

Francis House was still a building site when Margaret Hickie commenced work as Head of Care. Amid the piles of bricks and scaffolding, she was also embarking on a large-scale project of her own. She had to build a team ready to welcome the first children and families a few short months later. A monumental challenge for Margaret, who wasted no time getting straight down to work.

'My job at that time was to set up the hospice from a nursing and medical point of view,' she recalled. 'I started work on 1 June 1991 when the hospice was incomplete. It was hard to envisage what it would be like since it was still a building site and I was looking round with a hard hat on.

'There were virtually no staff when I arrived. There was Sister Aloysius and Sister Austin, who were involved in the planning, and Father Tom who'd been very influential in fundraising and getting the money through the Diocese of Salford for us to open. Sister Aloysius became Administrator and Secretary to the trustees.

'I was quite excited, but it was daunting in a way because I had to be the one looking to recruit staff. We had a local medical practice involved with the hospice as well. We'd already got a number of applicants and held interviews in my first week. They were conducted in a room at the adjoining offices of the Catholic Children's Rescue Society.

'We also visited Martin House in Wetherby, the only other children's hospice in the north. I was really struck by them. So were the Sisters and we modelled ourselves on them. They were very supportive because they really saw the need for more children's hospices. On a weekend off, I went to Helen House in Oxford, to see how that was also running.'

Margaret had been to Helen House before. She was shown round by its founder Sister Frances Dominica before the world's first children's hospice opened in 1982. 'It was in the process of being built and I remember having a hard hat on and going up step ladders with Sister Dominica as she talked about her vision for the hospice,' recalled Margaret,

who worked in paediatric care in Oxfordshire before moving to Manchester to work at Booth Hall Children's Hospital. As a qualified paediatric and general nurse, she was a perfect fit for Francis House. It was through a chance conversation with Sister Maureen, one of the Sisters asked to give up the convent, that she found out about the vacancy.

Margaret explained: 'I went to train as a health visitor in the mid 1980s and did that job for four years. That's how I met Sister Maureen who was a student nurse and she told me about the plans for a hospice which sparked my interest. I had a caseload of 200 families in my role as a health visitor. While there, a new type of health visiting began which saw us working closer with families.

'Rather than always giving advice, we'd get stories from families and encourage them to tell us what they were doing with

Directors of Care. From left, Margaret Hickie, Gill Bevin and Sharon Doodson

their children and what they were capable of. We treated parents as the experts on their children. I had that philosophy in mind when I came here. I even remember during my interview being asked about my vision and maybe I was the first one to talk in that way. Most hospital nurses then had a prescriptive-type role. Obviously, there's an initial need to show someone how to look after children with new illnesses, but these youngsters had these illnesses for a long time.

'Their parents were looking after them at home with very little help, if any, and they'd got their own way of caring for them. We wanted to make the children feel as though they were at home as much as possible, so that's how it worked. I realise the way of working may have changed at Francis House since I retired in 2009, but I'm pleased to know the philosophy is still the same. I think the Sisters also had that idea after visiting Martin House where the same principle applied.'

A total of 14 nurses and nursery nurses started work in October 1991, with a further seven other successful applicants joining the following January. A physiotherapist, art therapist and chef were also recruited. Margaret said: 'The new staff hadn't been able to see the hospice when they came for the interview, so it was difficult for them to imagine what it would look like. There were no others close by for them to have seen so they might have envisaged it like a hospital, or an adult hospice.

'I remember them all being astounded and delighted when they finally saw it. They said what a beautiful place it was and how homely it would be. It was more like a hotel. The philosophy was different to what they may have expected. They weren't going to work as nurses, or as a physio, in a traditional way. Only the chef would work conventionally.

'Everyone else had to share their skills. They wouldn't be wearing uniforms and they would be working alongside families, discarding some of their professional methods if you like. We didn't want them to direct these parents into what they should be doing, or looking after children how they thought best. They had to learn from the families, find out how the parents were looking after children and try to look after them exactly the same way. That was a big learning curve for a lot of the care team at first.'

By the time Margaret took up her post, some 20 families had expressed an interest in using the hospice. 'One of the interviewers at my job was Dr Clarke, a consultant neurologist. He was very helpful assessing the condition of children to decide if they were appropriate for Francis House.

'I also visited them all at home to look at their needs and find out what sort of care they required. I spoke to their parents and told them about the vision of the hospice and how it would be. We accepted all those children. All were appropriate. Once we were established, a lot of people wanted to use Francis House and would refer children with disabilities who didn't necessarily have a short life expectancy. So, we had to really look at what we were about and try to explain to people.

'We accepted children with life-limiting illnesses from birth up to the age of 16. We did take some profoundly disabled children whose lives were limited from the point of view of their severe disabilities, but usually we took children who had other complications as well.'

The big question everyone wanted answered was related to when the hospice would open. When would families actually come through the door for the first time? Margaret said: 'After we'd decided who we were taking and once the hospice was built and fully functioning, I can remember Sister Aloysius asking me when I thought we could open. I said the end of October. The families arrived a week after the staff to give them a few days' training and to make sure they were comfortable with what they were doing.

'I remember the first youngster we welcomed on the official opening day was a teenager with Batten disease, a metabolic disorder. It was a progressive illness, as were many conditions. Fortunately, he lived for a long time. Other children arrived on the same day and more during the course of that first week. The families were overwhelmed by their experience here. They didn't know what to expect, so had no idea what a children's hospice might look like.

'A few said they felt like they were met by a wall of love and warmth. No one rushed them or forced them to do anything. They weren't put into a hospital bed, or anything like that, so they couldn't believe it. They were fed by the chef, as were the families who came to stay as well. A lot of people felt respite was your child being taken away from you and there's a lot of emotion around that which people don't always want to do.

'So, families could come as well and that was an advantage in two ways. It suited them because they could see what we were like. They could be looked after and fed, but we could also get to know their children through the families. We did have paperwork that helped the families. I had devised a care plan to find out from families every little thing to do for their child and to document it so when there came a stage when a child, or young person, visited by themselves we would still be able to care for that child in the way the family would.

'They were assured seeing how we were working alongside them. Some stayed a few nights, some slightly longer. Martin House didn't have a uniform, so we went along with that. They wore tabards, but we decided not to enforce that. The first 20 children had a variety of illnesses, some of them metabolic. Some had very complex needs right from the start with many profoundly disabled.

'They might have to be tube fed, either through the nose, stomach or neck. Staff had to learn to look after things like that. The disabilities affected children in lots of different ways. Their breathing could become problematic and very early on we had children with ventilators coming. That was something some of the staff found really difficult, but we had a team with a variety of skills so people taught each other, as well as learning from parents and the hospitals we worked alongside.'

Initially, the seven-bed hospice was not full at all times, but demand soon increased. 'We didn't have that many children on our books at first, as they were being referred gradually. Most families wanted weekend stays because their children went to school. But as we got more and more children coming, it became difficult to always allocate weekends.

'We'd have no children here in the week and the Sisters really couldn't understand why we didn't have any children sometimes. But we had to explain that people wouldn't suddenly trust us. They have to hear from other people what it's like before they will decide to come.

'In addition, when people mention a hospice it's a big thing to accept that your child may have that need. They also don't know what a children's hospice is like anyway. We started getting overwhelmed very quickly. There were more and more children. The quiet time was useful for staff as it helped with training and getting used to the children.

'Then the numbers gradually increased and probably within six months, or maybe less, we were full a lot of the time. By the end of the first year, I think I was reporting we were approaching capacity. We had one boy

An owl swoops in on Francis House to bring joy to youngsters

Margaret Hickie introduces Princess Diana to families

who was fully ventilated and unconscious. It had been decided by the hospital it was no longer appropriate to ventilate him. In other words, they felt they couldn't do any more for him and we agreed he could come here. The hospital removed the tube and the ventilator.

'He started to breathe again and lived for quite a few years. I did wonder whether, with some of these children who come here, it's that feeling of love and warmth and they can relax more. Maybe it's more than that. When someone asks how long they're going to live, you just can't say, can you?'

'Right from the beginning we had young people who wouldn't see themselves as children. That needed to be addressed and eventually Francis Lodge was opened for teenagers and young adults. All the presents people bought for us were for young children, like dolls' houses and rocking horses. That was obviously nice, but people perceived that we catered just for young children which wasn't the case. Youngsters were outliving their life expectancy.'

Margaret spent 18 years at Francis House and her part setting up the facility for the first influx of families should not be underestimated. She was at the cutting edge of a pioneering care facility and laid the groundwork for future developments, including eventual expansion.

Quite rightly, she takes great pride in her pivotal role in the Francis House story. 'We were the fifth hospice to open in the country, but the quickest from the time of the idea being mooted to actually opening. Yes, it was very hard work, but what we were able to do was amazing and overwhelming. We had a child who came from Scotland and we realised straight away there was a need for more children's hospices and more were beginning to open.'

Inevitably, the first death at Francis House was a sad occasion. A girl with cancer of the brain had been referred by The Christie.

Margaret said:

'The day she was due to arrive the Macmillan nurse came to us and said her mother's washing had fallen off the line and it was the last straw for her. We were asked if we could wash the clothes for her. The washing was brought round in a taxi and we did it. Those were the sort of things we did for people as well. It wasn't just the nursing care.'

Gill Bevin – Director of Care and Registered Manager 2009–2020

Gill Bevin owes a lot to the youngsters of Francis House. They persuaded her to give up her job as a hospital sister to join them at the hospice. It was in 2002 that Gill took their advice and left the neurology ward at the Royal Manchester Children's Hospital where she had spent two decades working happily as a registered nurse.

Gill never looked back from the moment she walked through the door of Francis House until she retired some 18 years later, eternally grateful for those patient recommendations.

Gill said: 'Many of the children who went to that hospital at Pendlebury also came here. They used to tell me about the hospice all the time. I was a ward manager on a really busy children's ward. They weren't all little ones, with some aged up to 20. They were telling me about this fantastic place, called Francis House, and that I really should come here because I'd love it.

'They gave me that insight. As far as I was concerned, the children were a great advertisement for the hospice and were a big influence on me coming here. At the hospital, I'd worked in intensive care, neurology and the metabolic and endocrine unit. We also had oncology children on the ward as well. That, to be honest, makes up a massive part of the cohort of children who come here.

Gill Bevin played a key role in expanding Francis House

'So, my hospital experience really informed me about the children here and their types of conditions. I looked after them at the hospital when they were four, five and six and was looking after them here when they were 19, 20 and 21. So I also had a long history with the kids who came here.

'They may have a long-term terminal condition, but that doesn't mean they're going to die imminently. Someone with Duchenne muscular dystrophy, or spinal muscular atrophy, might be diagnosed fairly young, but they're dying in their twenties or thirties and maybe even beyond now because things have probably moved on.

'I'd reached a stage in my career at the hospital where I felt I was ready for something different. I kept hearing these things from these amazing young people who blew me away with their knowledge, confidence, mannerisms, bravery and just how down to earth they were. They kept saying: 'You'd love it there.' Things happen for a reason and I thought, maybe this is the time.'

Gill was to become a key figure during the expansion of Francis House, although she only

Having fun with the mobile sensory unit

just beat the deadline to apply for a vacancy on the care team. Gill explained: 'I'd known one of the staff from Francis House from the days we were both student nurses. She came on to the ward at Pendlebury and brought a young girl who needed a portacath fitting, a procedure which couldn't be done at the hospice.

'I'd had a horrendously busy day and was almost trying to crawl towards the exit. The staff member from Francis House had also had a long day but came in hopping and skipping. I remember saying to her: 'How do you look like that and I'm looking like this?'

It was a final little click. She said: 'There's jobs going, but the closing date is tomorrow.' I went home that night and maybe it was meant to be. I came to the hospice to get a form, went to work the next day and completed the form at home.

'My sister and I drove here and asked the receptionist to make sure they registered that it had arrived on the right date, the closing day for applications. I had an interview about two weeks later and came and worked here as a registered nurse on the care team. A couple of hospital consultants I knew thought this was a backward step and wondered why I was going to the hospice.

'I knew it was the right thing for me and once I arrived, I loved it within the first week. I'm not making that up. I thought this was meant for me. I was meant to be here.'

Gill joined the community team visiting families, a role which included handling end-of-life referrals. She said: 'My experience really helped with that, being quite autonomous and confident in the way we worked. That's the way you must be here. Sometimes you don't have lots of people you can call on –

you're at the top of your game and I really do believe that.'

Gill was also soon involved with the Seasons team for brothers and sisters of children and young adults with life-limiting conditions. She said: 'Obviously, we were aware of siblings at the hospital. I thought I was quite a good nurse there, but if I'm really honest on a busy hospital ward it's a bit of a nightmare when you've got kids with drips everywhere and little ones running around.

'However, when I came here I saw those same young children in a completely different light. I saw how their lives were affected by having a brother and sister with a terminal condition. It makes me come out with goosebumps because I had no idea really in the hospital. We used to get children in when they were acutely ill, get them better and they went home.

'Once I came here, I realised these siblings are carers at such a young age and live at such a high level of stress. What you don't know is that when they go to bed at night everyone is there, mum, dad and brother but they get up in the morning and they're gone.

'Grandma, or a neighbour, has come because the family went to hospital in the middle of the night. This is not a one-off. It happens a lot in their lives. Most little boys and girls go to bed and everything is the same in the morning. It's very different for these brothers and sisters.

'They live in a tremendous amount of stress. When I was a sister on the endocrine unit at hospital, we had little girls who started their periods and developed breasts by the age of nine, known as precocious puberty. There's an age for puberty – it shouldn't be too late or too early. When I came here, I noticed at the Seasons group that some girls had precocious puberty.

'I have no facts on this, but one of the predispositions for someone to get precocious puberty is a high level of cortisone in the body due to living at high stress levels and I could point out these children. Those kids didn't go to hospital to get investigated and the reason was because the other child in the same family may be in intensive care, or on a ventilator. So, someone developing breasts at nine is not a big problem because there's a sibling who is so sick. There are other reasons for early puberty, but one is stress and spotting this in the Seasons group was unbelievable.'

Siblings are a fundamental part of the respite care provided by Francis House. One particular session for a group aged between five and eight sticks in Gill's mind. Gill said: 'You don't think they take anything in but, in fact, they take everything in. They know more than you can ever imagine because they've overheard everyone talking.

'We'd all sit together either gluing, sticking or cutting things up and the conversation would probably make your hair curl. That sibling would be the only child in that entire school with a brother and sister who is likely to die before they reach adulthood. There's no one else like them there, because it's rare.

'Here, in the Seasons group at Francis House, guess what? You're a member of a club and everyone around you experiences similar things. Not quite the same, but similar and that's fantastic for them to be able to talk about those experiences.

'To sometimes say that they're annoyed at their brother or sister, or cross because they get all the attention, or they're embarrassed to bring their friends home. I once heard some kids, two with sisters with tracheostomies, chatting generally. One said: 'I never bring any of my friends home for tea. I don't like it when 'gob' comes out of my sister's mouth when she coughs and I'm embarrassed while my friends are there.

'One of the other children, aged about eight, said: 'We love it – we mark her out of ten to see how far the spit goes and if it hits the car windscreen, we all cheer.' They weren't embarrassed about bringing their friends home. They wanted her to spit. You could see what a difference the comment made to the other child. They had just re-framed something and put a different spin on it, in effect, saying, 'You can look at this in another way.' As an adult, I'd never have thought of that.'

Gill joined the senior care team in December 2008 and six months later took over as the head of care following the retirement of Margaret Hickie who had been instrumental in establishing and stabilising the hospice after its inception. The role was renamed director of care in 2011. 'When Margaret was retiring,

I thought, in for a penny, in for a pound. Blow it, I'll apply.'

Her previous managerial experience was invaluable, not just in the day-to-day running of the care team but also with helping the hospice develop. Gill said: 'When I took over Francis House was a seven-bed hospice. When I left in November 2020, we had built Francis Lodge which opened in 2014. We had also built up 463 on Parrswood Road and bought a property on Barcicroft Road this took a major amount of my time as director of care here.

'We started building the Lodge when I took over. In my ten years in this role, we were building and developing all the time. We knew the need was there. 463 belonged to Salford R.C. Diocese and we bought that. During the building of the Lodge, we discovered a problem with the dimensions.

'Once the builders went home one day, we went round everywhere in the evening with a piece of roofing insulation the same size and shape as a bed. The exercise was worth doing. It showed the builders would have needed to have taken off the corners of the walls to fit the beds in. The architects hadn't thought about the turn of a bed on a practical level. That was the level of detail we went into for the Lodge.'

In developing the Lodge users of the temporoary Lodge at 463 were consulted on the appearance and function of the facility. The Lodge was a parent-free zone, exclusively

Gill Bevin outlines development plans to families

for young adults rather than younger children. Gill said: 'It was important we had separate rooms for brothers and sisters, or friends, of these young adults. Children would share a bedroom in Francis House, but by the time you're 13 that's not okay, especially with personal care.

'We opened rooms named Manchester and Salford purely for brothers or sisters of a similar age, or friends. That's vital because it means everyone has their own space, PlayStation and bed. However friendly you are, or however much you like your sibling, you don't want to spend 24 hours a day together. It's really important for teenagers to maintain friendships and relationships.'

Gill looks back on her Francis House days with enormous affection. 'I've enjoyed every single job I've ever had. Maybe not every minute of every day, but I've enjoyed every job I've had. This job, I loved.'

Sharon Doodson – Director of Care and Registered Manager from 2020

Uniforms have never been worn by the care team at Francis House, a tradition which started the day the doors first opened. The intention was to make children and their families feel more at ease. There are more than 50 members of the care team, a dedicated group of highly trained professionals which includes nurses, carers and nursery nurses.

All come under the supervision of Director of Care, Sharon Doodson, who

Sharon Doodson became only the third Director of Care in 2020

took over in 2020, becoming only the third person to hold the most senior care post after Margaret Hickie and Gill Bevin. Sharon is honoured to work with such compassionate, selfless colleagues who look after 573 families in various ways.

She said: 'We all play an important part. There's no hierarchy and no uniforms either. We don't have those barriers that might be created by a matron or ward sister wearing a uniform. Everyone works together and it's a full team effort, as we can't do one thing without the other. We all need each other to achieve what we do and couldn't do it on our own.

'The nurses hold a certain responsibility as they have a registration and oversee the management of medicines, while other care team members are trained to support them in that respect. Nurses can also learn from other members of the care team as they bring different skills the nurses might not have.

'This is a fantastic place. I wouldn't hesitate if any one of the care team were looking after my family members because they give phenomenal care and take pride in what they do. That makes my job a lot easier. You need to work here for the right reasons. It's a difficult job and you can't be here without being interested in the difficulties that having a life-limiting condition can bring, not only to the young person but for the entire family. You wouldn't get full joy out of your job unless you have understanding.

'We have families who come here and who are really stressed. They're used to arguing with health care professionals to get what they want. They're fighting constantly with Statutory bodies. We need to be a relaxing place for them and staff must understand that they're not shouting at them. They're just frustrated and angry. That means you've got to delve deeper and ask: "Are you okay?"

'It opens up all the barriers and walls they've put up. We're lucky we've got the time to ask them if they're okay, whereas hospitals don't have that advantage.' Sharon has personal as well as professional experience of Francis House. Her nephew has a life-limiting illness and receives respite care. Other relatives have also used its services in the past.

'I understand what impact hospices can have on families. The difference they can make. It's not just about end-of-life care. It's about the whole support of the family from diagnosis up to a child dying and beyond.'

Sharon, a trained adult nurse, joined Francis House in 2015. She was the Clinical Lead at the Lodge and the House before taking overall control.

'From the minute I walked in I just loved it. It grabbed me straight away, the thought of providing holistic care for the whole family, supporting them and having the time to care. Sadly, the NHS doesn't give you that opportunity as often as you'd like it to.'

Once on the senior care staff, Sharon worked with the education team. That involved training staff to look after children with complex clinical needs safely and includes basic life support techniques and competencies around looking after youngsters who need breathing machines, due perhaps to a tracheostomy or who have a gastrostomy.

Whole Family Care

Francis House offers an extensive care package free of charge. It is delivered both at the charity's premises, as well as out and about in homes of families requiring support. Families can have several overnight respite stays at Francis House during the year. The duration varies from two to seven nights each stay, depending on family needs.

Children can stay on their own, or with their family depending on their individual wishes.

Sharon said: 'As well as looking after their clinical needs, we try to do as many activities as we can with the children. We do things that they're going to enjoy and make memories for when they go home.

'These are often things they can't normally do at home, which might be due to the equipment they need or the size of their home. Some of these children spend all day in bed because they're not able to get out and about. We also have a homecare team who provide respite care. This gives parents light relief in their home so maybe they can go out for a meal or do some shopping without having to take the child with them.

'The home team may also visit a child in hospital to give the parents a rest. Parents are reluctant to leave a child's bedside while they're in hospital so we'll go and sit with the

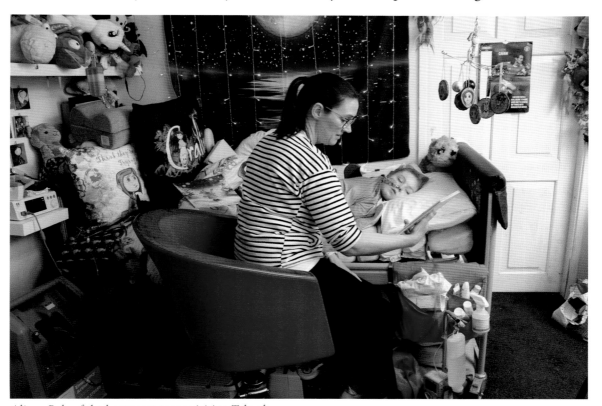

Alison Pyle of the homecare team visiting Tehyah

child. That allows the parent to go to have a shower or do whatever they need to do to get a bit of rest. The homecare team also does activities with a child while they're in hospital.

'In addition, they also provide end-of-life care support in the home, assisting other community teams. They might also arrange for the child to come into Francis House if the child needs to be here for end-of-life. We have an emotional support team offering help to children and young people on an individual basis. If a child is aware of their condition and knows what's going to happen then they have someone they can talk to. The team also offer bereavement support.

'We have parents' groups so they can chat to us and share concerns, while our Shining Stars group is for siblings of children who have died. That programme lets them talk specifically about their feelings and helps them with their grief. We also have the Seasons team who look after the siblings of children and young people who use the hospice. We probably do a group session once a month and also provide one-to-one care.

'Siblings can really suffer if they have a brother or sister with a life-limiting condition. We not only look after the sick child, we really take care of the siblings as well. Their situation can inevitably have a real impact on their health as they grow older since they're dealing with stress all the time.

'We see through their behaviour that they don't know how to handle what's going on. They don't know whether mum is going to be there the next day, or whether they're going to be in hospital with their brother or sister. There might also be anger towards their sibling because what's happening may be taking all of the attention away from them.

'So, when they come in for respite we allow siblings to stay as well and have staff who look after them. They might even do simple things like taking them to the Trafford Centre which they might not normally get the chance to do. There's real importance placed on the sibling, in addition to the sick child. People have a misconception that they want to look after their brother and sister, but that's the last thing they want to do because they do that all the time at home. Siblings get to do fun things. It's just about them and they get a lot of value from that.'

Homecare is unavailable on Sundays at present, but there are plans to provide a round-the-clock service every day. Typically, the homecare team looks after more than 100 families, providing respite care in all kinds of situations, including at times of crisis.

Flexibility is part of the culture. Families can stay with their child at Francis House if they want. Sharon said: 'We have six flats and families can stay with their child, or leave them here. A family might stay in a flat, but then go out for a meal in the Didsbury area. They may go out for a date night, things they can't do at home.

'We also have a flat for parents whose child is at the end-of-life stage. This has two bedrooms attached and a living room. It means families have their own enclosed space and grandparents can stay if they wish.'

Rainbow Rooms

'We have three Rainbow Rooms for when a child has died. We don't need to have known that child. It could be the hospital rings and lets us know they have a family who want to use the Rainbow Room, which they can.

'A family can go into the Rainbow Room, which is cooled to mortuary standards, as often as they wish until the funeral. Sometimes families don't want to stay but want their child to be here so we look after them until the funeral and give them that dignity. It's their choice and every family is different. We can adapt individual care to whatever their needs are.'

Children with life-limiting illnesses need to be referred before the age of 16. Sharon said: 'Parents can refer a child themselves or they can be referred by a medical professional. We then send off for medical information and as long as they have a life-limiting condition then they're accepted. Sometimes a child can be referred for social needs, but we're not the right place for that.

'Francis House is for children with a life-limiting condition so they're expected to die before they reach their early 20s. That age has increased; it used to be much younger. With a lot of these conditions, children are living longer than they once did, but with these illnesses they're still going to die sooner than an average person. Once they're accepted on to our roll, then they stay with us. We don't have an upper age limit.

'Some places have a cut-off age at 25. They're no longer able to use a children's hospice, but we don't have that. They can stay with us as long as they need to, either up until they die, or until they choose not to use us any more. That's why we have Francis Lodge, which is a parent-free zone for young people from the age of 13. We have activities appropriate for their age. Teenagers want to be treated like typical teenagers, even if they have complex needs.

'They may want to stay up until 4 am and get up at noon and have a bacon butty or a pizza, and they can do that at the Lodge. Teenagers have different routines and might snack at odd times, so the care team will cook for them if the chef isn't on duty. We're flexible to accommodate their needs.'

Families who use Francis House come from far and wide. They could live in a town which has its own hospice, but that does not prevent them from still coming to the Didsbury facility.

Sharon said: 'We do have families with another hospice in their area, but they choose to come here. As long as they're not using another hospice, because we're all charities, we have to make sure everybody gets a fair share of accessing a hospice. What we don't want is one family using five hospices.'

Francis House is well known for its warm and welcoming environment and activities which have engaged and entertained youngsters over the years. Two pods turn into cinema rooms, as Sharon explained: 'Big screens come down and light up with surround sound to give that cinematic experience without actually going to the cinema.

'A lot of young people are in quite big wheelchairs and depend on machines which are quite noisy. They feel uncomfortable going to the cinema because they don't like people looking at them. We also have two sensory rooms at both the House and Lodge, so children with complex needs can go there and have massage therapy for relaxation. We also have a hydrotherapy pool.

'Two computer rooms are adapted for different needs. We have what's called an "eye gaze" so they play games with their eyes. It means if they haven't got the dexterity to use the equipment, they can use it in another way. We also have virtual reality play sets, in which a child uses goggles. We have two art rooms for creative therapy, either drawing pictures or making things. There is also a massive garden outside with a pirate ship, accessible for wheelchair use. Adapted swings also give wheelchair users that rocking experience.

'We look after children with all types of conditions, many of them undiagnosed. We have neurological, neuromuscular or genetic conditions. It's varied and there isn't one more predominant than another. We don't do

A creative therapy session

as much oncology care as you might think. There is the odd case. Oncology specialists tend to want to keep their patients under their control, giving them hope of cure.

'They're looked after by a palliative care team who don't want to mention the word hospice as if to suggest they might not survive this. With cancer they're trying to give hope all the time. Children with cancer would benefit massively by coming to the hospice because there's so much support we can give them, even while they're going through treatment. But they tend not to come, whereas the highest percentage of patients at adult hospices are oncology cases. There are more children who can utilise the hospice who don't.'

A study by Dr Lorna Fraser, a world-leading researcher in child health and palliative care, showed a significant rise in children in England with life-limiting conditions over a 17-year period until 2018. The figure rose from 32,975 to 86,625.

Sharon said: 'The numbers are massive, but a lot of these children don't utilise a hospice. We're forever expanding and trying to build up our care team to open up even more bedrooms so that we can provide more respite care. We never turn anyone away. End-of-life is obviously prioritised and even if it's a family we don't know, we'd move mountains to get them here quickly.'

For Sharon, her respite from mundane admin work is seeing children taking part in activities. 'The children bring you so much joy. I do a lot of my job in the office stuck to my computer doing research and lots of reading and writing policies and procedures. It's important but often not that interesting, so to give me that joy back in my working day I do a walk round and see these young people to remind me why I'm doing it. I only have to spend two minutes with them and I've got a smile back on my face. Considering what they're going through, and all the challenges they're facing, they are phenomenal. They just spark joy – you can't help but get joy from every single one of them.'

Jackie Graham – Senior Care Team

Jackie Graham holds a unique place in the history of Francis House as the longest serving member of the care team. She reached a major milestone in October 2022 when she clocked up 30 years at the hospice. An incredible achievement which is testament to her devotion to the children and families who have been touched by her tender loving care.

'I've no regrets at all,' declared Jackie, reflecting on her decision to join Francis House all those years ago. 'The time has flown by. I can't believe I've been here for 30 years. It's strange to think I've been here that long. It's an amazing place to work and one day is never the same as the next.

'Even if you're looking after the same children and young people, the next day can be so different. You never know what you're coming in to because of the different types of things we do. The joy of simply playing on the swings, or giving complex nursing care, or ensuring a bath is luxurious and relaxing, or offering emotional support to siblings.

'Children are unpredictable, aren't they? You might go out on a trip one day and the next they may be seriously ill. It can be very fast-moving.'

Jackie is a highly respected member of the senior care team and joined the staff within 12 months of the hospice opening. Her service was only interrupted by two maternity breaks. After the initial intake of nursing and care team members either side of Christmas 1991, Jackie was among the second wave of recruits several months later.

Jackie grew up in Bath where she worked in a children's respite home. She had earlier qualified as a nurse in nearby Bristol, caring for patients with learning disabilities. Jackie said: 'I saw the post at Francis House advertised in *Nursing Times*. I had friends up here and was looking for a job in this area. I applied and

was lucky enough to be interviewed by Sister Aloysius. She was lovely, an amazing person. Sister Aloysius was very driven and focused and knew exactly what was going on, even if she wasn't there.'

Head of Care, Margaret Hickie and Robin Wood, Chair of the Trustees, were also on the interview panel. Jackie said: 'We didn't have anywhere near as many families staying in those early days when we only had seven bedrooms instead of the 14 that we have now. The bedrooms are split between the House and the Lodge and the building is completely different to what it used to be like.

'Because there weren't so many people coming, they tended to stay much longer because we had the capacity. Having said that,

Jackie Graham

Flashback to 1998 as long-serving care team member Jackie Graham shows her creative skills

we did have people travelling a long way to be looked after because there weren't many other children's hospices. Families would come down from Scotland to see specialist doctors based in Manchester and stay overnight here. Consultants are probably spread much further afield now working in hospitals, but at that time they were very much Manchester-based.'

Jackie became part of the Seasons sibling support group. 'It's such a huge thing because we care for the whole family, which is really important. These siblings are split into younger and older age groups and meet

about seven times a year. We have a five to nine-year-old group, while the other group is for children aged nine and upwards. As we evolve, we're also starting to support 16-year-olds and older.

'An early memory was taking 26 siblings on a coach trip to Rhyl for a weekend away in the mid 1990s. Siblings of children in wheelchairs don't usually get the opportunity to go on a beach, so to have that freedom and be able to run on the sand was special for them. Siblings stay over and are well looked after. One day I could be running around playing football in the garden, or having a really in-depth conversation with a sibling, while the next I could be looking after their brother or sister who might also need nursing care.

'Most siblings who visit don't have a disability. There may be some with the same condition as their brother or sister, but generally they are referred themselves and stay here in their own right. Diversity has always been at the core of our work, ever since the Sisters decided the hospice would be non-denominational. Being with parents in the Rainbow Room* and being able to share some truly special memories is always a privilege.'

• Francis House has three Rainbow Rooms cooled to mortuary standards where the child or young person is able to remain until the funeral if the parents wish. Each room has its own lounge and adjoining bedroom with a small private garden.

Andrew Clarke – Senior Care Team

Long-serving carer Andrew Clarke knew what it was like growing up in a large family. He was No. 13 to be born out of 14 and has eight sisters and five brothers. It was a lucky number as far as Andrew was concerned, because his destiny was finding Francis House where he swapped one big family for another.

Reflecting on 27 years and counting at the hospice, Andrew admitted: 'I'm from a large family, so that's probably why I fitted in here. I'm used to hustle and bustle – it doesn't faze me. When I joined at the end of 1995, I think I was the only bloke working here on the care

team for a while. There might have been one other, but it didn't bother me because I was brought up with eight sisters.'

Andrew was a gardener in Didsbury when he began volunteering on the care team. It was four years after the hospice opened. He said: 'Living nearby, I always wondered what it was like here and saw they were looking to enhance the team. I'd never done anything like it before and when a full-time position came up, I had to decide whether to continue with my gardening.

'I decided to put myself into this and it's been amazing. Quite honestly, it took me about half an hour to know this was for me. I realised there's something special going on here and I want to be part of it. That was 27 years ago and I still get the same feeling. I never get the feeling "Oh, I've got to go to work." Ever. It's a joy to come here.'

Days out with children have provided Andrew, a senior member of the care team, with countless memories. A favourite haunt for youngsters is Chester Zoo. He said: 'A long time ago I took a young lad who was here for end-of-life care to the zoo because his mum wanted him to see the monkeys. She'd never been able to do it, so we organised it and two of us went with his mum and dad. It was just before he died, but he got to do it.

'About three years ago his mum turned up at the Memory Day we have each year when we invite back all the families who've been bereaved. It took her 20 years to be able to come back into the building. Fortunately,

Andrew Clarke

I was there. She didn't recognise anyone else, but she recognised me.

'As a carer, you feel like you're helping someone on a journey. It's not a journey that they realised they were going to have. A parent has a certain vision of what their child's life is going to be like. Then, all of a sudden, when a child is born the family realise it's not going to be like that. It's going to be like this. You can't stop that journey, but you can help them along it. It's that real sense of satisfaction that you've actually done something that's been worthwhile and helped someone. Some children and young adults stay for a weekend, some for five or seven nights, while others are here for end-of-life care.'

Unsurprisingly, trips out are hugely popular with the children. Andrew said: 'We go to the beach at Blackpool, or to the play area or football pitch in the local park. We're in a really good position here in Didsbury since we can access many things. There's a cinema complex, restaurants we use all the time and we're always at the zoo. I remember taking a young lad called John, who had muscular dystrophy, to see *Apollo 13* when it came out at the cinema. John wanted to see it, so I said I'd take him there. Someone drove us to Belle Vue and we watched the film. Sadly, John is no longer with us.

'A lot of people say that they couldn't do our job. That's the typical response we get when they ask what we do for a living. They then want to know what Francis House is about and that's good because we need to get the word out about what children's hospices are like. People think there are rows of beds with dying children in them, but that's not the case. There's a lot of living going on at a children's hospice. Parents can stay over with their child and often do when they come for the first time. But gradually they won't stay any more because they trust us.

'That initial building of trust is really important with the parents. They need to feel comfortable you can look after their child and they can go home or do something else. There has to be trust between the parents and us. Siblings can be really upset when they go home. I say: "Why are you upset?" and they reply: "Because this is the best hotel we've ever stayed in."

'The conditions of the children who come here are more complex than they were because children are living longer with the illnesses due to advances in medication and technology. But the basic care of looking after someone never changes, because we're still here for them and for the family.

'A lot of our care will revolve around a child's basic needs, including feeding, medication and bathing. If the family stays, you obviously also make time to chat to them because they need to talk to people.'

It is obvious after a few minutes in Andrew's company that he has lost none of his enthusiasm after all these years.

'There's a lot of pride in this place. People are proud to work here. You might not get that elsewhere, but you have to understand it's not just a job. If you did think that, I don't think you'd last very long. It's about the whole

ethos of the place. The families who come here become part of the family. That's how I view it.

'The hospice has totally changed in appearance since 1995, every single bit of it. Every room has changed function over the years. There were seven beds initially and apart from growing in size we've also massively expanded what we do. We now have homecare emotional support, a Seasons group for siblings and a Shining Stars group for bereaved siblings.

'Support is also available for carers, recognising they too might need help coping with what can be seen as a stressful job. We're really well looked after. We have outside supervisors who come in and you can chat about problems and they give you strategies about how to deal with stuff.

'But you always have to remember that any grief that happens here isn't your grief, it's their grief. It's really sad because with children it's the wrong way round, isn't it? But you have to put it in perspective. We're seeing a family at the worst moment possible in their life, especially when they're coming here for end-of-life care. But if you can help them through that, that's where you get your emotional support from, that you've actually helped someone.'

As part of the charity's open policy, all new families are shown one of three Rainbow Rooms where a child or young person can stay until the funeral if parents wish.

Andrew added: 'I always say to new carers, especially when someone is using the Rainbow Room, that is the worst thing that's

The Rainbow Room where families can spend time with their child after they have died

ever happened to that family. There's nothing you can say that's going to make things any worse. The next worst thing is going to happen next week when they bury the child.

'We're in there alongside them. Families we've never met use the Rainbow Room; their child may have died in hospital and this may be the first time we meet them.

'That's always more difficult than when you've known someone for a few years and built up a relationship, but then that's what we do. I've all sorts of memories of the children and young adults I've met here. Some are the most hilarious people I've met in my life. Some are the strongest people I've ever met. We had a young lad, Stephen, who had a completely twisted little body, but up in his

head he was one of the smartest people I've known. Four children in the family had the same condition. Three girls and a boy, all of whom have now died. Stephen was a funny, amazing lad.'

As a senior member of the care staff, Andrew can spend much of his time undertaking administrative work, such as clinical governance, Care Quality Commission issues, auditing, staff training and appraisals.

He said:

'All that office work is vital, but I also still do my shifts on the team looking after the children. That's the most important bit to me, because that's where I get the most satisfaction.'

Claire Armstrong – Care Team and Seasons Group

Coming from the TikTok generation is a distinct advantage for Claire Armstrong in her role at Francis House. For a start it means she knows what is trending for the kids of today when she is looking after them.

'Social media in general is a huge part of the lives of older children,' said Clare, who is part of the care team and helps run the Seasons siblings' group. 'I know TikTok, whereas some of our older staff might not. Other big talking points for youngsters include Netflix,

football and the music they're listening to. I can relate to youngsters' interests and during our Seasons training we stress the importance of getting onto their level.'

Claire graduated from Manchester University in 2018 with a degree in Early Years and Childhood Studies. She has become an integral part of the care team, bringing a fresh, youthful approach to the mix. 'At first I thought being younger might be a barrier, especially for parents, but that's not been the case,' she added. 'The reaction has actually been quite positive and I've built up a good rapport with siblings.

Maira Williams (left) and Claire Armstrong from the care team with members of the Seasons sibling support group

'I didn't know a lot about the hospice before I came here. My dad, Peter, knew a lot more than me and was really proud when I got the job. I've learned on the job and it's a lot different to what I expected.

'You hear the word hospice and think it's going to be a sad environment, but that couldn't be further from the truth.

'It's an amazing place full of laughter with fun things going on and music. It's a happy place to be.'

Claire runs the Seasons team with Maira Williams and Sarah Laird. 'We'd love to grow the team and support more siblings, having more days with them,' added Claire.

'In the last 18 months we've started one-to-one visits in addition to our monthly group sessions. Brothers and sisters can feel a bit shy in a group setting, or maybe they've got extra things going on they don't want to discuss in the company of others.

'We might meet in a coffee shop, a park, go for a milkshake or ten pin bowling, or go for a walk.

'I enjoy working here and every day is different. It's a challenge but very rewarding and I get a lot out of it. You can see the positive impact on families.

'You have to keep a professional boundary, otherwise you wouldn't be able to do the job. We're not going to make anything better. Families are going through the worst thing when they've lost someone, we just have to help them where we can.'

Esther Lowery – Registered Nurse and Homecare Team

Nurses like Esther Lowery represent the future of Francis House. At 28, she is part of the new generation of carers meeting the needs of families. Esther splits her week between shifts at the hospice and working on the homecare team, led by Alison Pyle. Meg Dayan and Rachel Ellis make up the homecare team.

So how will Francis House look in a few years' time? Esther believes individual services like homecare, emotional support and the Seasons group will expand, resources permitting. Esther said: 'We're trying to offer families what they want based on individual needs, rather than just one thing that fits everyone.

'We've just started a baby and toddler group here so parents can meet other parents who are in the same boat. Homecare has developed massively in the last year or so and the role has changed. In the past, homecare might have been looking after someone at home for a few hours.

'Now there are different parts to it, particularly around developing end-of-life care at home and giving a parent a choice whether they want to be at home or in the hospice. That involves working alongside different health care community teams to support the family, including symptom management for the child.

'When a child is referred, parents also tell us that they want support for the sibling and emotional support so demand for those services is also increasing.'

Esther qualified as a nurse in Leeds, working on a general medical children's ward before specialising in paediatric intensive care until joining Francis House two years ago. She said: 'I moved to intensive care at the Royal Manchester Children's Hospital which was great for learning lots of skills, some of which involved end-of-life care, but a hospital wasn't where I wanted to be.

'I wanted to come somewhere with time, resources and a nice environment which can provide really good end-of-life care and meet all the needs of families and more. To help children meet their wishes. You can't really give that in an intensive care unit. It's a privilege to be able to do that here. To be there for families at the worst time of their lives and to do it as best as we possibly can.

'Every family is completely different and although we're going to find it emotionally challenging, at the end of the day that's what I'm here for. I want to be there for that family. We receive a lot of support and can see a psychologist every six weeks or so. It gives us a chance to reflect on feelings and emotions. There's definitely a lot of support to make sure we can cope because obviously it's heavy stuff with difficult conversations.

'There's enormous job satisfaction, especially when you get it right and feel you've done everything you possibly can and parents are so grateful.'

Esther Lowery

CHAPTER 8

BEREAVEMENT

It didn't take long for Natalie Hands to realise the value of respite care offered by Francis House. The mum-of-two was among the first wave of nurses recruited in October 1991. As one of two nurses on the first night shift, she saw for herself the challenges faced by parents caring for a severely sick child on a daily basis.

Natalie said: 'We looked after a boy and a girl who couldn't sleep because her condition meant she had spasms. Her parents slept in the flat at the end of the corridor, but the whole idea was to let them rest and we did whatever needed to be done.

'The girl, who was nine or ten, couldn't speak and my colleague and I took it in turns to hold her in a certain way on our knees all night to stop the spasms. As soon as you put her down, the spasms would start and there was no medication to stop them. We told her mum in the morning what she'd been like and she said: "Yes that's exactly what it's like at night, and that's how we hold her as well."

'It struck me that this is what parents have to go through every night. There were two of us to share holding her, but for a mum on her own it must be so difficult. Another time a mum wondered if we could look after her severely disabled son who had been referred to us. She wanted to go to the theatre for the evening to see *Les Miserables*. It was soon after we'd opened, so we only had a few children here and there was quite a good staff-to-children ratio, allowing us to get to know the families.

'Two of us were looking after him and we couldn't take our eyes off him. His breathing was terrible and we tried to amuse him and keep him comfortable. We were trying to clear mucus from his mouth, yet his mum had seemed quite relaxed leaving him with us. We hoped he was alright. A lot of families now have suction machines to clear mucus and medication is different, but in those days many families had to manage on their own.

'He seemed fine and couldn't really communicate, so we had to get cues from facial expressions. His parents came back, saying they'd had a lovely evening. She said it was quite normal for her son to be like that and the mum, dressed in her finery, just picked him up and carried him. She had learned to cope with how he was.

Natalie Hands with mum Sarah Wood and Devon

'We got to know him in the years to come. His breathing was helped by a tracheostomy and they obtained a suction machine to clear his mucus. Machines would have existed in hospitals, but not at home. Once again, we saw how normal his mum was with him, whereas we'd been watching his every breath. He came like that so it wasn't a sudden deterioration. But it showed what these families have to cope with at home and it was nice his parents could go for a night out.'

Natalie had returned to work part-time after her children reached school age. She had trained as a children's nurse originally and was alerted to a vacancy at Francis House by a friend.

'I found myself getting excited about the thought of working at a children's hospice. I'd been on a nursing refresher course and had a hospital placement where you just didn't have time with patients at all. It was very task orientated and I didn't think it was for me. When I heard about the concept of a new hospice with time to be with the children, I thought that was brilliant.'

Natalie became one of the bedrocks of Francis House where she spent more than a quarter of a century before retiring in 2017. She went

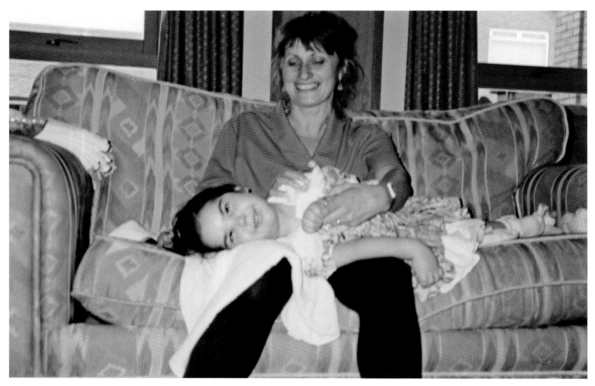

In safe Hands… Aimara receiving loving care from Natalie

full-time when she took over as Clinical Lead at Francis House in 2010 and one of her proudest achievements during her career there was setting up bereavement support for families.

She realised straight away that it was needed. 'The first child who died at the hospice was a girl of about 10 who came in with her younger sister and baby brother. We were well staffed because we were in the early days and a lot of people were looking after the girl who was sick. I was drawn really to the sibling and spent time playing with her and we had a good rapport between us.

'Her sister died and we looked after the family. I think seeing the sibling made me aware what it must have been like for brothers and sisters. The change in the family and what it's like when a child is ill and parents have to be focused on them and not their other children.

'I had this interest in bereavement and did a counselling course. Thanks to a donation, Sister Aloysius had funds to allow me to take a diploma in bereavement counselling. Martin House, a children's hospice in Yorkshire, had set up a bereavement group for brothers and sisters and they put on a course for six of us from Francis House.

'They told us what they did and how support had developed. The six of us, nurses and other members of the care team, put together a case for a bereavement sibling support group and Sister Aloysius allowed us to go ahead. My colleague Jeannie Bratton, who sadly died in 2022, was involved. At one of the pilot groups, we asked the kids what they'd like to call it and one of the boys suggested the name Shining Stars. Children came once a month on a Sunday and we'd discuss what grief is like, how to handle emotions, how to talk about grief and taking memories forward.'

The Shining Stars group for bereaved siblings was set up in the mid 1990s. Until then bereavement support was conducted on a more informal basis, with staff keeping in touch with families. Natalie split her four-day week between the care team and bereavement support. She would visit bereaved parents and a support group for them was established around the same time.

'I didn't really understand what grief was like, apart from my own experiences, and what it does to your emotions and how different people respond. It's not a set thing that everyone goes through. It's the impact on family life and we saw families split up because of how grief affected them. Sibling support was much better in a group format. We'd get a child to talk through activities, like stories or art, rather than talking one-to-one.

'Quite often they'd be the only bereaved child in their school, whereas once they came here they just used to gel as a family. We had older and younger ones and by the end of the first session the smaller children would be sitting on the older child's knee and they'd look after them like brothers and sisters. It was

just amazing. By the end of the first session, they'd got that bond because they'd already had a similar experience.

'Parent sessions were held mostly at home, or Francis House or elsewhere. It gave the opportunity for mums and dads to talk about their own feelings. Sometimes that was the first time someone would hear what it was like for their partner who couldn't share their feelings until a third person was present. We'd visit some parents before a child's death to talk about bereavement. But that was very hard for them because there are losses upon losses.

'A parent will experience a lot of losses before a child dies. Loss of the child's future they hoped for; loss of capability as they became more limited. They were dealing with a lot, so we mainly focused on bereavement after the child had died. We'd support parents for up to two years and left them in control over when they wanted us. Support would start from about six weeks after death as in the first few weeks they receive a lot of support from family and friends and then that starts to taper off.

'We had a fluid, flexible way of supporting people to fit in with their personalities and how they were coping. By saying up to two years it gave them an idea that they weren't going to be feeling better in six weeks' time and to pace themselves. We helped them understand how grief works, what was happening and how to handle emotions, feelings and what works for them. So, it wasn't prescriptive.

'Families would often say to us: "Would you go and see her? She needs bereavement support." Effectively, they were saying, "Will you see her because we don't know how to fix her, she needs fixing." But we weren't there to fix people, only to walk with them through this natural process.'

The bereavement team started the Memory Day which is held each spring; it began as Rainbow Day in 1994. It opens with a service of hope at the nearby East Didsbury Methodist Church where the names of children who have died in the previous five years are read out. A buffet is laid on at the hospice where activities are provided for children. Parents can revisit the rooms their child might have stayed in if they wish before a lighter end to the day which might take the form of a magician providing entertainment.

Natalie said: 'It's a lovely day and families who have lost a child, or young adult, in the last five years are invited. They can come for the whole day, or any part. They don't have to come and some whose child died longer than five years ago will also attend. It's quite an emotional day and can be draining for families who come and cry together and remember.'

The chapel at Francis House also has a Memory Book. Families are invited to fill two pages with words and pictures dedicated to their loved one. The book is optional, acknowledging that people grieve in different ways. As Natalie said:

'Sometimes people aren't ready to grieve and there are other issues stopping them. That's part of bereavement support. You just have to be sensitive to what else has gone on in their lives.'

Natalie took over as full-time Clinical Lead during a reshuffle in 2009, following the retirement of Margaret Hickie as Head of Care. Gill Bevin became Director of Care with an overall strategic role, as the hospice was looking to expand. Five years later Francis Lodge was opened. Gill and Natalie handled responsibility for operational aspects, duties which involved staffing, rotas, referrals, talking to parents and overseeing training. Organising the diary to accommodate families wanting respite care was critical. Natalie said: 'As you can imagine, weekends were very much in demand. That's when the rest of the family could do something together.

'We had to make sure dates were given out evenly. We also had to keep space in the event of an emergency if there was a family crisis. Quite often a social worker who was aware we offered respite at Francis House would phone you to say something had happened. So, we had to juggle where we could.

'Sometimes parents might go away on holiday and leave the child with us. Other times they'd all come as a family. The same families would do all those things. For some families, respite was coming to the hospice and having meals made for them and not worrying about washing, cleaning, ironing or anything else. They would come for a much-needed break as well and enjoy a good night's sleep.

'I felt it was the right time to retire in 2017. I loved working for Francis House and I loved the job. It was exhausting sometimes and had its frustrations like any job but I loved doing it and getting to know the families and the kids. I saw people go through the worst experience in their life and loved to see them come through it, knowing there was somewhere like the hospice they could tap into at any point.'

Kevin's Final Journey

Railway enthusiast Kevin made a final poignant journey to honour his love of trains. Kevin's ashes were put into the boiler to power a steam train on East Lancashire Railway. His final resting place was a fitting send-off for Kevin who had muscular dystrophy and died in December 1999, aged 20.

His funeral service in the chapel at Francis House where he received respite care also had a railway theme. 'The train now leaving platform ...' was the familiar station announcement at the end of the service, followed by the puffing sound of a steam engine. After cremation, Revd David Ireland led a memorial service on the station platform at Bury as a locomotive powered up.

Kevin's ashes were scattered in the engine furnace and the journey included a stop at the village of Summerseat where a tree was planted in his memory. A funeral tea was then served for mourners in the station master's office at Ramsbottom.

Bob the Builder fixed it for Cameron – true to his famous catchphrase. 'Can we fix it? ... Yes, we can!' was the rallying call and theme song of the children's hit TV show which became a million-selling number one hit. Bob the Builder was also Cameron Jones' favourite programme, so it was only appropriate that Bob and his love interest Wendy attended his funeral in 2010.

The two characters from the Lego store in the Trafford Centre were late arriving at Trinity Audenshaw Church, leading to a 30-minute delay for the service. David Ireland conducted the service and then went on ahead to Dukinfield Crematorium to await the funeral cortege.

Understandably, it was a little slow getting there since Cameron's coffin was placed in a JCB digger, just as Bob would have approved. David recalled: 'I was stood there in my gown and this "jobsworth" at the crematorium saw a JCB coming towards the entrance.

' "You can't bring that in here ... this is for hearses," said the official, to which David promptly replied: "There's a coffin in the bucket, therefore it's a hearse."

Cameron was six when he died in 2010, having been diagnosed with a brain tumour at the age of two.

Mum Kimberley raised funds for Francis House to thank them for looking after him. She said: 'After a 15-month stay in hospital and a huge battle, life was a little scary. I was about to take home a little boy who I knew was never going to grow up. My very own Peter Pan. When we were introduced to Francis House it was like a fairy godmother had waved a magic wand and everything started to seem a little easier than I'd first imagined. When it was time for my little boy to gain his angel wings, staff were on hand 24/7 and they made sure that every last dream we had came true.'

Nathan is a Shining Star

The Shining Stars group for bereaved brothers and sisters helped Nathan. He was nine shortly after his younger brother Oliver died in September 2015, aged just five.

Oliver was born with a life-limiting condition called Wolf-Hirschhorn Syndrome and was introduced to Francis House as a one-year-old, along with the rest of his family.

Dad Darren said: 'It was a lovely atmosphere. Everyone was really friendly and we saw parents, children, and staff interacting with everyone. We didn't know anybody else with a child like Oliver, so when we came to Francis House we didn't feel so alone.'

Mum Jayne said: 'Having a child with special needs, your home becomes like a hospital. You've got equipment, monitors, oxygen and you've got tanks around the house in case of an emergency.'

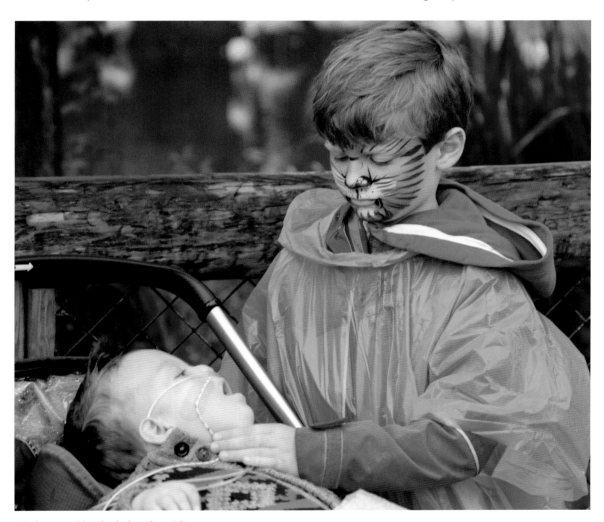

Nathan and his little brother Oliver

Oliver had spent long periods of his short life in hospital and was again admitted to intensive care after catching a cold. After his death, the family wanted to be at Francis House and the hospice team settled them into one of the Rainbow Rooms.

Jayne recalled:

'They put Oliver in bed with his pyjamas on, still caring for him even though he had passed. The rooms are lovely, there's a little bedroom with a lounge off it and friends and family can come and visit.'

While the family were grieving, Nathan was cared for by staff who gave him the opportunity to talk and ask questions.

Darren said: 'It just gave us that little bit of breathing space that we needed. I don't know anybody else who's been in our position burying a child. You need the help. They've been through this process so many times, and they just know what to say.

'Nathan had his ninth birthday just after the funeral. At Shining Stars, he was able to meet children in exactly the same situation and who he'd already made friendships with. Other friends might have lost a grandparent, or maybe even a parent, but there are not many kids who have lost a brother or sister.'

Jayne added: 'Just coming back and seeing the staff and feeling cared for in his grief meant a lot to him because he'd not been forgotten.

'It was really nice to come back to the Memory Day,' said Darren. 'Meeting other bereaved families and seeing the staff. You've been through so much together, it's great to catch up and to see how everyone's doing and remember.'

Mum and dad Jayne and Darren

CHAPTER 9

KIRSTY HOWARD

The history of Francis House is littered with examples of amazing bravery shown by boys and girls of all ages. None was better known than Kirsty Howard, who melted the hearts of a nation with her infectious smile and bubbly personality. An extraordinary little girl from an ordinary background in the suburbs of south Manchester who won a host of famous admirers and became a star herself.

Prime Ministers, sporting greats, pop icons, business tycoons and even a King and Queen were enchanted by the charity fundraiser who defied medical experts and put Francis House on the map. Kirsty was born in September 1995 with her heart back-to-front, a complex condition so rare it did not even have a name. At that time, there was only one other similar – though not identical – recorded case in the world, in Australia.

Her first visit to Francis House was in February 1999, aged three and a half. Kirsty was not expected to live for more than six months. Sheer determination pulled her through, a quality shown by countless other youngsters to have come through the doors of Francis House. Kirsty lived until she was 20, and what an incredible life she led.

An unbelievable journey which revealed her huge spirit, character and courage. A life spent linked up to an oxygen cylinder, a necessity along with the nasal tube taped to

her cheek. Kirsty needed a heart and lung transplant but was too weak to survive the anaesthetic.

Her condition was so serious she had to be checked five times a night to ensure she was still alive. Kirsty's abnormality meant a number of her internal organs were located incorrectly and she underwent several dangerous major heart operations, almost losing her life in 2005 when she was given last rites. Kirsty once again confounded the medics and recovered.

Inevitably, throughout Kirsty's short life there were private lows as her health deteriorated, alongside the public highs as her fundraising reached new levels. She became a regular visitor, using the hospice to aid her recuperation after frequent hospital visits. She was always welcome and made many friends there.

With her sweet smile and obvious charm, Kirsty was chosen to spearhead a fundraising campaign for Francis House. A charity called the Kirsty Appeal was born. It was an inspired move. The campaign raised more than five million pounds, a staggering amount critical towards helping secure the long-term future of Francis House.

David Ireland, Chief Executive of Francis House, said:

'Francis House had struggled to meet its running costs for many years. Kirsty's fundraising changed that and gave us a measure of security that allowed us to expand and develop our service. Hundreds of children, young people and their families owe a tremendous debt to the young lady whose face made Francis House a household name.'

It cost roughly £1.4m a year at the start of the millennium to run Francis House. The charity received a total of £57,000 from five health authorities which was enough to pay for 17 days of respite care. The rest had to be found from donations. A lot of the credit for the success of the Kirsty Appeal deservedly went to Susie Mathis, a former singer, radio presenter and freelance fundraiser.

Susie saw something special in Kirsty and, with the blessing of the youngster's parents Steve and Lynn, turned her into the face of Francis House. Her mum and dad readily agreed to Susie's request because it meant helping many other children with life-limiting illnesses. Incredibly, the long-running campaign, skilfully co-ordinated by Susie, became one of the most successful in the history of charitable fundraising.

Susie had been recruited to raise funds for a Rainbow Millennium Fund. But instead, it was the Kirsty Appeal which took off. A *Times* photographer took a picture of her on the lawn at Francis House with her oxygen cylinder

The iconic image of Kirsty Howard which led to a major fundraising campaign

behind her. It was a picture that painted a thousand words. The next day Kirsty was all over the newspapers. The power of the press had helped Francis House.

The Times donated a baby grand piano to the hospice for the music room and it still has pride of place to this day. Kirsty had already appeared in the newspapers as part of a controversial and hard-hitting advertising campaign.

The strap line of the advert read:

'The only way a terminally ill child like Kirsty will benefit from the lottery is if she wins it.'

The dig was in response to repeated refusals by the National Lottery to allocate money to Francis House.

One of Kirsty's first fundraising engagements was to hold hands with her idol David Beckham as they came onto the pitch at Old Trafford before the England football team played Greece in October 2001. She was the England mascot and Beckham, the country's captain, was so moved by her courage that a firm friendship began.

Celebrity endorsements were crucial and Susie went straight to the top of the A-list. The World Cup qualifier was arguably Beckham's finest hour in an England shirt – he scored a

Beckham's Angel Kirsty

Please support Kirsty's dream to raise £5 million to secure Francis House Children's Hospice. This would be an everlasting legacy to Kirsty's courage. Telephone 0800 097 1197. Registered Charity No. 328659

Little Kirsty handing the final Baton to Her Majesty the Queen at the Opening ceremony of the Commonwealth Games on 25th July 2002

Kirsty helping Ronan Keating to switch on the Blackpool Lights, 2002

By royal appointment... Kirsty mixing in famous circles

memorable goal with a last-minute free kick and described Kirsty as his lucky mascot. The next month he accompanied wife Victoria to Kirsty's Angel Ball, the charity's highest profile event of the year in Manchester.

The following year signalled an iconic moment featuring David and Kirsty. The occasion was the Opening Ceremony of the Commonwealth Games at the City of Manchester Stadium where Kirsty was chosen to hand the baton from her beloved Becks to Queen Elizabeth II. The late Queen broke with protocol to walk down steps to meet Kirsty, who was six at the time.

Her royal engagements also included a meeting with King Charles III at Buckingham Palace. Kirsty had been nominated for a children of courage award and was introduced to the then Prince Charles. He gave Kirsty a book he had written and after a short chat, he knelt to read to her. But Kirsty simply said: 'I have had enough of you. Goodbye.' Charles laughed and walked off.

Kirsty was never one to stand on ceremony, greeting Prime Minister Tony Blair at Downing Street with the words: 'You must be Tony.' The pair walked hand in hand into the White Room, used for entertaining heads of state, to eat Jammie Dodgers. Kirsty told him: 'You have a posh house.'

David Cameron was another occupant of No. 10 whose life was touched by meeting the leading lady of Francis House. Meetings with high-profile politicians gave Kirsty's supporters the chance to push the case for a greater share of government money for children's hospices.

Kirsty's role in that national advertising campaign had highlighted the issue. Susie

Mathis said at the time: 'It is ridiculous that a little girl has to fund a campaign to get money. She is terminally ill and in and out of hospital all the time. I'm hoping the advert will embarrass people and make them consider where the lottery is being spent and the vast amounts its bosses are paying themselves in bonuses.'

Kirsty saw every new challenge as a milestone to achieve. And there were many such occasions for the girl whose dainty smile and fragile body was recognisable to millions. On and on she went, turning on Blackpool illuminations with singer Ronan Keating, meeting stars from *Coronation Street* and sporting legends like rugby World Cup hero Jonny Wilkinson, who presented her with the Helen Rollason Award for Courage in 2004.

Chris Roberts, Chair of Trustees, was struck by Kirsty's bravery. 'As I arrived, I saw this small girl charging through reception with a plastic tube up her nose, being hotly pursued by someone carrying an oxygen cylinder. That was Kirsty Howard. She was a little dynamo and continued to be so for the rest of her life,' said Chris.

The rich and famous showed love and support. Among them was Harrods owner Mohamed Al Fayed, a charity patron. He generously handed over £120,000 when the appeal started. The tycoon donated £5,000 a month initially to Francis House to cover nursing staff costs. That monthly figure tripled eventually.

Mr Al Fayed also kept a large photograph of Kirsty in his office. Susie said: 'He gets a donation out of anyone who asks who the little girl in the photo is. He got £3,000 out of Burt Reynolds. Kirsty loves him and treats him like an uncle.' Mr Al Fayed handed gifts from the shelves of his department store in London to Kirsty and other Francis House youngsters.

He said the privileged had a responsibility to help the less fortunate. On a visit to Francis House, he said:

'It's part of life to give an example to others who can't afford things, to share what God blessed them with. If you are privileged and you have extra money, then you give to the needy and the poor. What they do here is angel work. What they do here is very, very important.'

The fundraising appeal reached its £5m target on a momentous night at the Hilton Hotel, in Manchester, in October 2006. Kirsty entered her own fifth and final Angel Ball in a stunning white satin handmade gown to the strains of 'You Raise Me Up' and with decorations of angel wings circling above.

A spine-tingling evening reached its climax when Kirsty got on stage to sing her favourite song, Ronan Keating's 'When You Say Nothing At All.' As she sang the opening lines, guests were stunned to hear the voice of Ronan himself, who glided through the crowds to join an ecstatic Kirsty for a duet of the song live on stage.

Mr Al Fayed had supplied a helicopter to take Ronan from an appearance on the BBC's *Strictly Come Dancing* show directly to the event. But the fundraising did not stop there. The Kirsty Club was set up and continued to attract donations, helped by opera singer Russell Watson, a long-time supporter and friend. The pair had met at the ceremony to launch the 2002 Commonwealth Games.

Near the end of her life, Kirsty used Francis Lodge where she found help and comfort, having done so much herself to assist others. The tireless fundraiser was training to be a teacher to help children with special needs. She held a special *Alice In Wonderland*-themed party to celebrate her 20th birthday.

A month later she passed away. At 1.38 am, on Saturday, 24 October 2015, in the intensive care unit of Manchester Royal Infirmary, Kirsty finally succumbed to her condition. Her parents and sisters Zoe and Kim were at her bedside and she died peacefully, leaving amazing memories and an incredible legacy.

Needless to say, David Beckham was among the first to pay tribute to Kirsty, posting a moving tribute on his Instagram account. He said: 'Words cannot describe how amazing this young lady has been over the years. Kirsty has been defying doctors for many years and while doing that she has been raising millions of pounds for terminally ill children.

'I met Kirsty in 2001 when she became the nation's and my own good luck charm for the game against Greece. We also met the Queen together in Manchester so you could say we have spent some amazing moments together over the years. It was an inspiration to meet such a brave young lady with so much drive for helping others.'

Tearful family friend Susie Mathis also led the accolades. Susie said: 'It's just dreadful

Kirsty enjoyed her respite stays at Francis House

losing Kirsty, who was so inspirational and vibrant and has done so much and raised millions of pounds. Her legacy will always be there. She's helped so many people. This little girl is extraordinary. I can't get my head around the fact she's gone.'

The then Prime Minister David Cameron shared a picture on Twitter of himself with Kirsty. He said:

'She was an amazing person with boundless passion who did so much good.'

Kirsty had raised £7.5m in her short life and she was given a fitting send-off. Crowds lined the streets and broke into spontaneous applause and cheers as her pink coffin, pulled by two white horses draped in pink and white silk cloth, travelled to the church in Wythenshawe, Manchester. Mourners included *Royle Family* actress Sue Johnston, who gave a reading at the funeral service, Russell Watson and *Coronation Street* stars Samia Ghadie and Anthony Cotton.

The world said goodbye to the miracle girl whose magic rubbed off on so many.

CHAPTER 10

CHILDREN AND YOUNG ADULTS

The opening of Francis Lodge fulfilled the dying wish of Stephen Ryan. He wrote a moving letter to the trustees in 2009 explaining that he wanted to be cared for in an adult environment. His muscle-wasting condition meant he was increasingly isolated as he got older and he came up with the idea of a place for teenagers and young adults.

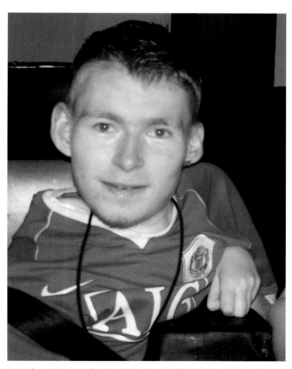

Stephen Ryan, the inspiration behind the Francis Lodge extension

Stephen told how he needed to spend more time at the hospice as his deteriorating condition was making it harder to keep in touch with friends via computer. He died a few months later, aged 21, but his request was not in vain.

Almost a year on, his sister Tanya, who had the same condition, cut the ribbon to officially declare open a temporary four-bedroom building. She was accompanied by Manchester United goalkeepers Edwin van der Sar and Ben Amos.

The interim facility was located at No 463, Parrswood Road, Didsbury, which later became a residential unit for young adults with severe disabilities. (It had been Mount Carmel children's home previously.) The 463 facility was a forerunner to a new £3.5m extension which opened at nearby Francis House in May 2014.

Tanya Ryan with Manchester United goalkeepers Edwin van de Sar and Ben Amos

Francis Lodge met a growing need for respite care for older users. Significantly, the number of beds within Francis House was doubled to 14. Lodge users are aged over 13 and this parent-free zone gives young adults greater freedom and independence.

Stephen suffered from spinal muscular atrophy (SMA) which also claimed the lives of sister Natalie (18) in 2001; Stacey (20) in 2004 and eventually Tanya (23) in 2014. Their surviving sibling, Stephanie, was born without the condition. In his letter, Stephen proposed that a new facility could allow him to spend time with other young adults with life-limiting conditions.

It highlighted the changing needs of young people as their conditions worsen and lives are affected. Educational, social and health needs must be adapted during the switch from child to adult services. Tanya said later: 'Stephen would have been so proud at the opening of Francis Lodge and, ultimately, the new extension. He would have been amazed and even though he's not here, I know he's watching his dream come true.

'He was determined to see a place created to meet his needs and those of his friends and to live a life like anyone else rather than one governed by routine. I just take each day as it comes and my friends and family get me through. I don't think any of us could have coped without the support of Francis House over the years. It's like a home from home.'

The Ryan siblings, along with parents Bridget and Steve, visited Francis House for respite care from 1993 with the hospice helping them through the deaths of four of their children. Chief Executive David Ireland said: 'Stephen's letter brought into focus the plight of many young people who are too old for the children's service, but too young to fit in with the traditional adult care system.

'Even though the creation of Francis Lodge from the receipt of the letter by the trustees to the official opening took only 18 months, it was too late for Stephen, but his friends and many others have benefitted from his efforts and will do so even more in the future.'

A new era in the life of the hospice began when Francis Lodge opened in 2014. Two years earlier, the first of five cornerstones had been laid by Sir Alex Ferguson, the then manager of Manchester United. The link with Old Trafford came through the Manchester United Foundation, a charity partner of the hospice. The football club helped the hospice raise more than £600,000 during the association.

United player Jonny Evans was also on hand as Sir Alex laid the cornerstone with the late Nathan Sturgeon. It was a day to treasure for Nathan, a big United fan and a user of the hospice, who assisted Sir Alex to lay the stone. Sir Alex was so touched by Nathan's courage battling muscular dystrophy that when he died in January 2016 he went to his funeral. Fergie kept a low profile standing at the back of the church in Westhoughton, near Bolton, when he paid his respects.

Other hospice users Kate Snape, Kyle Wells and Kirsty Howard also laid cornerstones. Kate joined Sarah and Barney Storey, both Paralympic cyclists; Kyle accompanied the Lord Lieutenant Sir Warren Smith, while Kirsty was alongside Camilla Al Fayed, representing her father Mohammed Al Fayed, who funded the salary of a nurse at the hospice at the time. Sister Austin and Father Tom laid a stone in memory of Sister Aloysius. Unfortunately, Tanya Ryan was too ill to attend the ceremony.

The topping out ceremony was conducted by *Coronation Street* actress Sally Dynevor and Tayyeb Sheikh, a sibling who used the hospice. Two years on from welcoming the first young adults, the Lodge was officially opened by the then Duke and Duchess of Cambridge in 2016.

The interim lodge, located at 463 Parrswood Road, gave staff and young adults the chance to help Manchester University

Francis Lodge was completed in 2014

research what facilities would be appropriate. Experiments included the types of sinks and even staff rotas. David Ireland said: 'We've introduced a twilight shift. The young adults may want to stay up all night, lie in all morning and have a bacon sandwich at 2 o'clock in the afternoon! We need to be able to cater for that.'

In 1996, the hospice had only one child over the age of 16 using the hospice, but by 2014 that figure had reached 87. There are now more than 180 young people over the age of 18. David added: 'It's become an issue around the country. Many hospices can't cope with the amount of young people needing palliative care. We talk about transition a lot, but there is nowhere to transition to.'

Parent-free Francis Lodge has no upper age limit. All seven bedrooms have en suite bathrooms, with two flats for siblings or friends. The hospice had expanded to meet an increasing need from families, both at the hospice and at home. But that also meant added costs.

By the time the new building opened, running costs totalled £4.6m annually, of which around 15 per cent came from government funding. That compared with costs of £3.5m before the extension. Some adult hospices received up to a third of their income from the government. 'If we could get a third of our income from public funding we'd be quite happy,' said David. The Lodge features a terrace providing access to an outside space at first-floor level, a recording studio, a games and computer room, a cinema room and a large lounge overlooking a lawn.

Kyle Wells

The Kyle Wells story is truly inspirational. He cried when he first came to Francis House at the age of six as he wanted to go home. An understandable reaction from a child frightened by the unknown. Before long he shed more tears – this time because he wanted to stay!

That was in 1995. Francis House is now Kyle's permanent home. He lives at 463, the charity's specialist residential unit on Parrswood Road. Now 33, Kyle has remained on the charity's books ever since that first emotional introduction.

He has minicore myopathy, a form of muscular dystrophy so rare he is one of only four people with the condition in the United

Kyle Wells is very much part of the Francis House family

Kingdom. Two need wheelchairs and Kyle is one of them. His condition was spotted before he was a month old, when doctors realised he wasn't wriggling about as much as a normal healthy baby.

Kyle said: 'My parents were quite happy to leave me here for four or five weekends a year, in the capable hands of the staff. At first, I was a bit wary of staying on my own, but someone mentioned that you can bring a friend when you're coming. My friends liked it as much as I did. So much so that even now they have great lifelong memories of this place. That says it all.

'At that point I would have lived here. Definitely. I got an awful lot from it, especially as I was going through difficult times at home with my family. My mum and dad had split up. My mum was a heavy drinker and had an abusive partner. Coming here was like just a complete shift in environment. I went from complete domestic chaos to complete calmness and feeling cared for.

'I got so much from coming to the hospice. It gave me that break from the everyday madness. My sister was 12 years older and had already moved out. After mum died in 2001 when I was 11, dad moved back into our house in Salford which was purpose-built for me. I was the one main stable in the house which seemed weird as a kid.

'I lived with my dad up until my mid 20s when David Ireland, the hospice Chief Executive, told me about his idea for 463, the residential unit. He asked if I fancied being on the short-list to be one of the first to move in. I thought, "I'm grabbing this with both hands" and thanks to David I was given this opportunity in 2014.

'Straight away, I thought I love it round here and I can't thank the people in the area enough for how they've been with me. I was the first one to move into 463, which is almost like a mini version of Francis House.

'They promote independence and luckily I've always been quite independent, so it comes naturally to me. Some of the Francis House staff have migrated over to 463, where the ethos is very similar, although the care is full-time. 463 is two semi-detached houses which have been knocked into one. There are seven of us there and it's very spacious. Staff cook meals for us and we can come and go as we please.'

Kyle's tough upbringing gave him great mental strength and he has not let the fact he cannot walk affect his outlook. He said: 'I've always been in a wheelchair and in a way that's better. I always think someone able to walk and losing that ability will be 10 times worse than never having it to begin with. It doesn't stop me doing anything. Even as a child, I was street savvy from the beginning. At seven or eight I played out like a normal kid and my mates didn't treat me any differently.

'I had plenty of friends around the area and felt safer round the streets than in my own home. As my mum was a drinker and her boyfriend was physically abusive to her, out on the streets with my friends was safe to me. Kids are always taught not to talk to strangers, your safe zone is at home. My world was the

Kyle with Gill Bevin at the launch of Francis Lodge in 2014

opposite way round. I never knew what would happen at home but, on the street, everyone was amazing locally.

'I didn't see that I was disabled once I got a wheelchair. The disability is being unable to get from A to B without a wheelchair. Once I had a wheelchair, then it was problem solved really. I needed my first chair when I was four when my first positive view of the world was formed. I'd just moved into the house in Salford and none of the locals really knew me because I'd just moved there.

'However, the minute they realised I needed money for a wheelchair they started fundraising. I wondered why people who didn't even know me were so bothered and I thought all people must be like this. From this moment I had a positive view of people in general.

'Mum and dad wanted me to go to a mainstream primary school, but without an electric chair it would have been impossible. I would have needed to have been pushed around in a manual chair. My parents didn't want me to go to a school for pupils with learning difficulties since I had no learning difficulties.'

Kyle was a good learner and went on to study animal care and film studies at college. In fact, he has got to know quite a few stars of the small screen and stories of friendships with celebrities are chronicled in his memoirs, called *Friend To The Stars*, a book available from his website friendtothestars.com

He has struck up friendships with *Dragons' Den* star Duncan Bannatyne and actor Jimmi

Harkishin, who plays shopkeeper Dev Alahan in *Coronation Street*. His entrepreneurial spirit also saw him meet professional wrestler Hulk Hogan. Kyle has a long history of overcoming the odds, most recently when he contracted Covid.

He said:

'The biggest problem with my condition is respiratory. The media presented us all with this fear so, when I got that positive test, I feared the worst. I didn't feel shocking but presumed that because of my condition and what I'd seen on the news the chances were I wouldn't survive it.

'I thought, if I get over this I want to do something positive to help as many others as possible, so I decided to write the book to show what can be done. I think with people in general it's just getting that penny to drop. I think you can do whatever you want, it's just having that confidence.'

Kyle has an amazing outlook on life. 'Because of my physical state, people presume it'll affect me mentally. But getting through the bad times gave me so much confidence. You're not expected to live your average life, but whatever you do as a kid is built into you and stays with you forever.

'You're programmed one way or another early on. Luckily for me, I was thrown straight in at the deep end and having a disability was the least of my worries. So, it never bothered me because I had so many other things to worry about.'

Jack

Tina had a normal pregnancy. But when her baby Jack stopped feeding and was crying constantly he underwent countless tests in hospital until he was sent home with a feeding tube. Four years later Jack was finally diagnosed with a rare life-limiting genetic disease and the family were referred to Francis House.

Mum Tina said: 'His immune system is on high alert constantly and fights his body. It's left him with some damage around his brain, so he's pretty much like a newborn baby really. He can't hold his head up and doesn't talk. He's fed by a tube but has an amazing smile and he loves his sister, Sophie. Jack has quite a wicked sense of humour and loves laughing.

'Francis House has helped us feel like a family. We can go out together and it's not all about the medical needs. It's somewhere you can just come, forget about that and remember what it's like to be a mum or a dad, rather than a nurse carrying out medical interventions. When you see how they work with the children here you wouldn't think twice about anyone looking after your kids.'

Jack and Tina with carer Gio Castro in the Snoezelen Room

Henry

Henry was born six weeks early and following complications with the birth was diagnosed with a number of complex needs, including quadriplegic cerebral palsy, severe brain damage and scoliosis. Mum Laura said: 'Henry is such a bundle of joy. I absolutely adore him. Obviously with his complex needs he needs a lot of extra care which means he comes with an instruction book basically.

'When we're at Francis House they have a place where the parents can stay. It's so nice to be able to relax knowing I'm with Henry, but not quite with Henry and know he's still got all the care and everything's in place for him. At Francis House, they don't just offer support for Henry but for me as well. It's nice to know that if I do need just to talk to someone, they're there for you which is nice because not everyone is.'

Faizan

Faizan was born with a life-limiting condition and first came to Francis House at nine months old. As a young adult, he now stays at the Lodge along with sister Inaya. Mum Tayyauba said: 'Faizan has already told us "this is my happy place" and that speaks volumes because you're more than happy to leave your child in a happy place.

'We've been accessing the hospice for over 17 years and I've gone from an anxious mum

Laura with 'her bundle of joy' Henry

All smiles … Dawn and Paul

to a relieved, relaxed mum. When I drop the children off, they're so excited to come, they look forward to it. The tables have turned because they want a break from us. We just love this place. What a transition it's been for us as a family because we all need that break from each other as well.'

Faizan said: 'I can see myself smiling when I come to Francis House and I feel like this is my second home.' Dad Asim said:

> *'Francis House made Faizan feel like a special person, not an ordinary person with special needs. To them he's an important person and they make him happy. That's the most important thing.'*

Paul

Paul has been coming for respite care for more than 15 years. He has severe cerebral palsy and seizures and as he's grown older his needs have become more complex. Mum Dawn said: 'The opening of Francis Lodge showed me that care wouldn't stop when Paul was 18. It continues, which is comforting.'

'I never doubted that the care in the Lodge would be different to the House. I knew you couldn't visit as a parent because it's a parent-free zone. Francis House has helped with my mental health, what I'm going through and my day-to-day struggles. Even looking after Paul, I still have my own problems. There are other things going on, so obviously I've had emotional support to help with that.'

Kate has been coming to Francis House since she was seven years old

Kate

'I have spinal muscular atrophy type 2 and need more physical help as I get older. Even though I'm only 25, I've lived longer than anyone expected. My last life expectancy I was given was 20. When I reached that age, I was at university and had a party called 'The Kate Didn't Die Party.'

'None of my friends could understand that, but when I come here they understand how big a deal it is for me to have lived this long. I found out at an early age that my condition would eventually kill me. That I would never get better and was always going to struggle physically, be in pain and get weaker.

'When I'm here I chat to the staff naturally anyway. I talk to whoever is on shift caring for me. We discuss whatever has been going on with me. If they think it'll benefit me they'll mention it to the emotional support team who'll call me, or we meet for a coffee so I can let go of all that stress for a while.'

Kerry Anne

Francis House has no cut-off age for care once a youngster under the age of 16 has been referred. Brave Kerry Anne is a shining example of that. She has Rett syndrome, a rare genetic disorder that affects brain development and occurs in about one in 12,000 girls born each year.

Kerry Anne first came for respite care in 1996, aged 10, and has enjoyed being part of the Francis House family ever since. Mum Anne said:

> *'I didn't know anything about Francis House, but we were welcomed as soon as we arrived. I immediately felt it was a very happy place and the staff were great. In all the years we've been coming they've helped me a lot. I don't know what I'd have done without them.'*

Anne has worked part-time as a phlebotomist at Wythenshawe Hospital for more than 30 years, taking Kerry to day care in the morning and collecting her after work to continue meeting her needs. There is no cure for Rett syndrome, but Kerry Anne's condition has plateaued and she is stable.

Anne added: 'We need support and Kerry needs 24-hour care but when she goes to Francis House for respite, she gets that care as well as a complete change of scenery and enjoys trips out with the care team. I'm thankful for having Francis House in my life all these years.'

Kerry Anne started receiving help from Francis House in 1996

CHAPTER 11

VOLUNTEERS WHO MADE IT ALL POSSIBLE

Amazing dedication by countless volunteers has kept Francis House going over the years. Endless stories of sacrifice show the huge amount of love and goodwill for the charity.

Pauline Armitage MBE

One of the most remarkable examples of commitment to the cause concerns Pauline Armitage MBE.

Incredibly, she worked for the hospice in a full-time capacity for 26 years without getting paid a single penny! Five days a week she made the 30-minute drive over Barton Bridge on the M60 to work in her office at the hospice in Didsbury from where she managed the charity's accounts. A 40-hour week for which she never once wanted recompense.

Pauline was just happy to help. She is so modest about her efforts she is even reluctant to discuss that unbelievable devotion. Instead, Pauline prefers to praise her fellow volunteers, recognising that without their collective efforts the hospice simply would not have functioned.

Pauline started volunteering at Francis House in 1992, almost a year after it opened. She stayed until 2019. She worked on reception on a Sunday afternoon and added two more afternoons once she retired from her job as a deputy principal at what is now Salford College. Hospice founder Sister Aloysius, aware of Pauline's considerable administrative skills, asked her to look after the bookkeeping.

So, she abandoned plans to take a master's degree in nursery education at Manchester University to focus instead on her charity work. It is fair to say that Pauline, together with her friend Tom Wood, helped take Francis House into the computer age in the mid 1990s.

Pauline Armitage MBE, one of many who has made an amazing contribution to the hospice

Tom, one of her college deputies, had retired just before Pauline and joined her at the hospice on Mondays. He stayed there as a volunteer as long as she did, putting his computer database skills to good effect for the hospice's benefit. Pauline said: 'When I started it was in the very early days of Francis House and most things were done with pen and paper. For example, receipts for any donations we received were recorded in a book with a pen which seems so out of date now.

'The hospice was starting to fundraise and getting names and addresses. It did use computers, but there was no database system. The two secretaries were working hard, but had lots of other things to do, so I started helping and it just grew from there really. I knew what to do as we'd used computer systems at college, where we had 70 full-time and 200 part-time adult education staff.

'Tom had been very involved in setting up computer systems and he started coming to the hospice. I'm not an IT person and was very dependent on Tom. It was more the admin skill that I brought. Our auditors were also pushing Sister Aloysius to get the accounts system computerised and link them up with programmes used by our accountants. We were able to keep better records and use the database for things like newsletters.

'My son John was doing a master's in information technology and he set up the first email addresses for Sister Aloysius, Sister Austin and Father Tom. That was great fun, especially trying to teach Father Tom who, right to the end of his life, was not computer-minded at all. Nevertheless, they all got an email address. Sister Austin was learning very quickly about computers, while Sister Aloysius wasn't particularly interested because she had lots of other things to do.'

Pauline was awarded the MBE in the 1980s for her work setting up the first Youth Training Scheme in Salford. YTS, managed by the Manpower Services Commission, was created in 1982 at a time of huge youth unemployment. An ambitious Pauline had left senior roles in Catholic education and was appointed area principal for Eccles, Swinton and Salford with a brief to develop adult and continuing education.

Pauline said:

'I was very interested in inner city youngsters and the problems they had. The docks had closed in Salford. Many youngsters didn't have two parents and dads were often unemployed, as were grandfathers, so there were no history examples. It was very difficult. The whole idea was that kids did college work and combined it with job training with employers. However, Salford didn't have many major employers, so it was hard to persuade small firms to take youngsters, even for one day a week. But we managed to set up schemes for girls and boys to work in care homes and school nursery classes and these were very successful, providing them with City and Guilds qualifications.'

Pauline had a family member who was a nun so knew about the Franciscan Missionaries of St Joseph and their work in the Diocese of Salford. 'I was very interested in the Order and the work Sister Aloysius was starting to do caring for children with a short life expectancy. I'd left Catholic education and wanted to give something back and there was no way I could have sat at home.'

Once involved Pauline could not leave, even turning down an offer from a sixth form college needing her experience to set up an adult education service. Pauline was awarded the Benemerenti papal medal in recognition of her voluntary work, an honour which took her by surprise.

Pauline's late daughter Margaret was in on the secret, discreetly gathering all the necessary background information needed by the Bishop of Salford for the award. Son John and Margaret were there to witness the proud moment the medal was presented by Father Tom at Midnight Mass on Christmas Eve when the hospice was 10 years old.

Pauline said: 'Margaret was a teacher and extremely talented. She used to make Christmas cards which were sold at the hospice and she got to know Sister Aloysius quite well. She was a good needlewoman and did jobs for Sister Aloysius and got on well with Sister Austin.'

Margaret was presented with a bouquet of flowers by Sister Aloysius as a token of her appreciation for all her work. Pauline has seen huge change at the hospice over the last three decades.

'It was a small family and like a home from home. It's much different to when I started there. Obviously as time has moved on things change and understandably the hospice is more security conscious. In my early years there, I could just go into the hospice and the chapel. No doors were locked, but that had to stop to protect the children.'

Pauline emphasises the contribution of fellow volunteers.

'We'd have been stuck without them,' she admitted. 'Volunteers did an enormous amount. They worked on reception like me, in the kitchen and in so many different ways. I also had two volunteers helping me with the accounts. We've had an incredible amount of help all the way through and I know those in charge would agree with that. I was very glad I was able to contribute and thankful I had that to fill my retirement.'

Pauline's support does not quite end there. In March 2021, she walked round the grounds of her retirement complex on crutches 90 times to mark her 90th birthday.

Her fundraising target was £2,000 – but she finished up raising an incredible £28,893, including an anonymous £20,000 donation. The funds were split between Francis House and the Alzheimer's Society.

Despite her lack of mobility, Pauline covered a distance of 22 miles in a month to complete the challenge.

Harold Addie

War hero and hospice veteran Harold Addie

The life story of war hero Harold Addie was quite extraordinary. He took part in the famous D-Day landings at Normandy, in northern France, on 6 June 1944. The young sailor was only 19 at the time.

As a Royal Navy wireman, he looked on helplessly from the deck of his ship as Canadian troops were wiped out by machine gun fire. While attacking the enemy on Juno beach, Harold's landing craft carrying the tanks and soldiers struck a beach mine, leaving the crew stranded for four days before the vessel was towed to safety.

An amazing story of courage and bravery. A devotion to duty which saw him serve Francis House with such distinction much later in his life. Harold, from Baguley, spent around 25 years as a volunteer and fundraiser for the charity until his death in 2017, aged 92.

He helped out on reception and in the kitchen at least twice a week and his daring antics saw him tackle numerous challenges, even as he approached his 90th birthday. He abseiled the North Stand at Old Trafford football ground in aid of Francis House and performed a similar stunt from The Big One roller-coaster in Blackpool in aid of soldiers injured in Afghanistan.

Harold walked from Land's End to John O'Groats and made a freefall parachute jump, aged 74. He undertook a coast-to-coast walk from Wales across England, a 670-mile adventure along national trails. He was accompanied by his loyal Jack Russell dog, Snowy. Harold penned a book about their adventure, entitled *Don't Forget The Dog*, which raised £5,000 for the hospice.

In 2013, he said:

> *'If I'm fit enough, I'll do something. I've had an eventful life, but I've enjoyed every minute. I feel slightly guilty because I'm still fit at 88 and there's nothing wrong with me, whereas a lot of people my age are in serious trouble with their health. Francis House has been like a second home to me. There's a family atmosphere and I look forward to going there. The hospice has made a big difference to my approach to life. I started to think of other things instead of myself and it was a wake-up call.'*

Harold met Betty at a Belle Vue dance hall in 1951 and the couple married a year later and had five children. For many years Harold ran his own business repairing domestic appliances, mainly vacuum cleaners, before handing over the company to son Martin. In the roll call of Francis House helpers, modest Harold deserves every recognition for his contribution, both to charity and his country.

Judy Bailey

Spectacular fireworks, nostalgic music and countless picnic hampers overflowing with endless supplies of food and drink. It can only mean the famous Arley Hall concerts! An unforgettable evening of midsummer madness which each year drew thousands of excited partygoers.

The event was set in the picturesque grounds of Arley Hall, a beautiful stately home nestled in the rolling Cheshire countryside. A social occasion not to be missed which ran for 14 years from 1994. And, as a fundraising event, a winner every time for Francis House.

The organiser was mum-of-three Judy Bailey, whose ambition and enthusiasm created one of the most successful fundraising campaigns in the charity's history. At its

height, the Arley Hall shows drew a crowd of 7,000, a staggering number of concertgoers for an event run entirely by volunteers initially.

It was all Judy's idea, as she explained: 'We went with other families to a firework and lights concert at Capesthorne Hall in 1992. I'd done the odd charity event and came away thinking that I could create a family event. Francis House was very much in the news then, because it had just opened. After I contacted the hospice, one of the trustees, Peter O'Brien, visited me at home. He was a great man who could see something in the idea. He said: 'Come on, let's build this idea, this dream you've got.'

'The hospice didn't have any money and needed some exposure to the public. But if it went wrong, how were they going to cope with hiring everything? Peter took it upon himself to underwrite the concert personally, so there was no risk to the hospice. That summer he had a heart attack, but he didn't want this idea to disappear so he put me in touch with a couple of contractors. A fellow volunteer, Millie Llewellyn, helped us create our first concert in 1994. The costs of putting it on came to just below £37,000 and after paying them off we made a handsome profit of just over £36,000. Peter's gamble had paid off.'

Initially, Judy used a company called Performing Arts, based in Bollington, before linking up with the Manchester Camerata Concert Orchestra and freelance conductor Tim Redmond. Judy wanted a Last Night of the Proms finale before the fireworks and, to add more fun, she introduced a Sixties

theme. Acts like Gerry and the Pacemakers, the Hollies, The Manfreds and tribute groups such as Fabba, the Bootleg Beatles and the Counterfeit Stones appeared over the years to make sure the night went with a swing.

The family concerts raised around £1m, a staggering sum. The record amount was £85,693 in 2003. Judy said: 'I remember one year, around 1996 or 1997, the police agreed to take the cash we'd raised to deposit overnight in their safe at Knutsford police station. There was around £28,000 and the superintendent rang me up on the Sunday morning and said: 'I think you better come and get your money pretty fast because we're only insured for £7,000 to £8,000,' so I went to pick it up.

Fun and fireworks at Arley Hall

'Pauline Armitage, who looked after our books, carried money in her boot one time. As the event grew bigger, we eventually got Securicor to pick up the money. We had so many crazy times. In the first or second year, someone lent us a caravan and my husband used to sleep on the money. We'd take it home the next day and lay it all out on the carpet to give us an idea how much we'd raised. We'd then bring it into the hospice on the Monday. We always got excited once we hit a magic number of ticket sales, because we then knew we were making a profit. There was a wonderful atmosphere at the concerts. You'd have proper picnickers coming along in black tie, carrying upside down trestle tables, full of platters of food. They'd have linen and candelabras.

'There were a lot of repeat visitors who came every year. It became such a family thing. The Sisters and Father Tom always came and set up a picnic – we were really lucky how well it took off. My office was at home and after school my daughters would help by posting out tickets. Millie would help with paperwork and everything that was involved, from the stage to the stewarding, parking to the bins and also the raffle. People came back year after year to help because they wanted to be involved.

'I was a bit of an old bag because I wouldn't let anyone have a drink until the concert had finished. Then we'd put out wine, beer, cheese and sandwiches which Francis House had kindly provided for all the helpers. We'd be on a high and have a babble and say a big thank you to everyone. We had fantastic fireworks and it was electric at the end.

'Once we grew beyond 3,000 people, it became a bit more stressful. People could pay on the door if tickets were available and I'm not sure we ever turned anyone away. The Arley estate was a beautiful setting. It was lovely, with the hall behind you. We always set out to get good raffle prizes. We tended to get a holiday, with flights, as first prize. The Arley event was somewhere families could go. Some of the children from Francis House came along as well. It was such a lovely warm feeling and at the end of the day you're helping such a wonderful place which, by the grace of God, many of us haven't needed.'

Judy intended to step aside, but Sister Aloysius persuaded her to join the charity's fundraising team on a more formal basis. By then, she had been joined on her concert committee by David Woodrow who became Fundraising Manager at Francis House in 2000. Friends Millie Llewellyn and Carole Geary, both fellow volunteers and fundraising stalwarts, were also on the committee.

Judy said: 'The whole thing had to become more businesslike. Today, we wouldn't be able to do what we did at those first few concerts. No one would have let me go off and have a bash at organising a concert like that because things have changed, especially with health and safety. It's hard to choose an outstanding memory. There's too many. I always thought: 'Wow, we got through that one, what a relief and we made some money.'

A Tatton Park spectacular in aid of Francis House

'It'd probably take a good six weeks either side to wind it up and wind it down and get all the accounts sorted. We'd start again in the January. We had one year when we had not very pleasant people around who came and scratched cars. Times changed and you had to start protecting oneself and your people more.'

Only one concert was cancelled due to rain, in 2007, when Judy and her helpers had to refund tickets. 'We were amazed by the number of people who gave a donation. Thankfully, we had insurance so the hospice was never out of pocket and, in fact, made a profit that year. That would have been our last Arley Hall concert as we knew it. We then linked up with Tatton Park where they held two concerts over one weekend each summer. A Last Night of the Proms was followed by a Party in the Park on the Sunday. The agreement at the beginning

was that we took the proceeds of the raffle on the Sunday only and we ran the corporate hospitality on both nights.

'Tatton could see we'd already got concertgoers from Arley on our database and perhaps they hoped some of them would go to boost their numbers. I guess they weren't foolish. That relationship lasted until 2013.'

Judy's support for Francis House did not end there. Far from it. Her tireless team also organised a series of annual balls over a period of 14 years from 2002. These also generated in the region of £1m for the charity. The Belfry Hotel, in Handforth, was an early venue followed by The Mere Golf Resort and Spa.

Each year had a different theme and almost every time the figure raised went up. It virtually doubled between 2008 and 2012 thanks to clever fundraising and, above all,

The Mere Ball in 2013. From left, Rachael Taylor, Charlie Ross, Gill Bevin, Lucy Thompson, David Ireland and Judy Bailey. Picture courtesy of Cheshire Life

the generosity of supporters. The record, achieved in 2014, was an incredible £129,857. All donations from live auctions went directly to the charity. Judy knew why the figure went up so dramatically.

'We decided to try to sponsor a nurse for a year by breaking the auction down to 12 months of the year with a salary auctioned, for example, at £30,000. So, we'd ask if guests would sponsor a nurse for the month of January for the sum of £2,500. A table of 10 guests might give £250 each, or a business person might put their hand up and pay the entire donation on their own. The idea flew. Every time it flew.

'If bedrooms needed new beds, hoists, baths or televisions, we started a section

in the auction for that equipment as well. Thankfully, the first year we did it we had back-up auction lots. So, the way forward after that in terms of fundraising was to break figures down, so it was obtainable. That's when it made a big difference. If all bedrooms needed new beds, or hoists, or needed new baths, we started a section in the auction for that. The experiences were really emotional. It was the same team of a few girlfriends, with maybe a few more on the ball. We also had Charlie Ross, a brilliant and much-loved auctioneer who did all the auctions at Mere.'

Other one-off events included concerts at Bridgewater Hall in Manchester, one hosted by the BBC broadcaster Richard Baker. An evening with John Stalker, the Deputy Chief Constable of Greater Manchester, raised almost £13,000.

> **The biggest single fundraiser in aid of the hospice was a show performed by comedian Peter Kay which raised an amazing £170,000. The Bolton funny man was persuaded by David Woodrow to appear in a special one-off show in a marquee on Chester racecourse.**
>
> **Judy said: 'I've never experienced anything like it. David went to an event in Manchester where Peter Kay was performing. David is always very lovely, but cheeky and he went up to Peter and asked him if he would do an event for us and Peter agreed to do it. We could have sold out two or three times. There must have been 500 people there, if not more. Privately, Peter kindly met one or two families of Francis House backstage and gave his services free of charge.'**

Judy looks back on her fundraising days with great fondness. 'I feel very privileged to have been involved. It was wonderful and I miss it. I just wish we'd had one final concert, but we didn't. I remember I'd have meetings with Father Tom and Sister Aloysius in the boardroom after I'd first met them. Father would sit opposite me and Sister was on my left. I was terrified because I was a complete novice. But what a pair. They were so supportive of everything I did. They were always there and came along to the events. I'm terribly lucky to have had those years. I was just a normal mum with a lot of friends. We just created this and came back every year to do the same.'

There was one night which did cause Judy embarrassment. A supporter offered to pay for a cabaret act which involved two men wearing German helmets – and nothing else! 'They were terribly clever, but I wanted to be a mile under the soil because Sister Aloysius, Sister Austin and Father Tom were all there. All I can say is, I'm so grateful they weren't sitting in the front row!'

Posh Nosh on the Menu

What have Sir Terry Wogan, June Whitfield, John Cleese, David Essex and Thora Hird all got in common? The answer is they all provided recipes for a fun cookbook to mark the 10th anniversary of Francis House. *Posh Nosh*, which included favourite dishes from almost 100 celebrities, was published by volunteers Carole Geary, Judy Bailey and Millie Llewellyn.

It was their idea to get the rich and famous to contribute. Carole took Sister Aloysius,

The Posh Nosh recipe book

Fundraisers Graham Baxendale and Carole Geary on a VIP train journey in aid of the hospice

Sister Austin and Father Thomas Mulheran to meet world-famous chef Raymond Blanc at his Manchester restaurant. Blanc agreed to promote the book and write the foreword and the venture raised a lot of money.

Carole, from Alderley Edge, began volunteering for Francis House in the mid 1990s and was part of the committee which organised the sell-out summer concerts at Arley Hall and Tatton Park. Carole organised countless fundraising events, including ladies' lunches, carol concerts, fashion shows, Christmas balls and even a VIP train journey.

Her infectious enthusiasm for fundraising, combined with the support of family, friends and a volunteer committee of women from Prestbury and Alderley Edge, has seen her raise hundreds of thousands of pounds. Carole describes volunteering as 'addictive.' She said: 'I don't feel guilty about asking for things to support Francis House. It empowers me and once people are on board my passion becomes their passion.'

Lawrence Millett

Car dealer Lawrence Millett liked nothing better than treating youngsters at Francis House to rides in his luxury motor cars. Bentleys, Hummers and limousines would arrive at the hospice to give excited children a quick spin around Didsbury. He even gave one teenager, Stephen, a lift to school one day in a Rolls-Royce. 'I feel like a drug dealer,' joked Stephen.

Lawrence volunteered at the hospice and became so attached to the families he cut short a business trip to the United States to attend the funeral of Stephen's sister Natalie in 2001. Lawrence sold exotic cars to the rich and famous and jointly owned Bauer Millett, a well-known dealership on Deansgate, Manchester.

Lawrence died of liver cancer in 2005, aged 61, and was renowned for his generosity to Francis House.

Sister Maureen FMSJ said:

'Lawrence was a volunteer worker and most generous benefactor, not to mention a true friend, to the sick children, their families and staff at Francis House.'

In the early years, Sister Maureen was responsible for in-house volunteers whose roles included the reception, kitchen and cleaning. She said: 'The volunteers were amazing and Lawrence definitely sticks out in my mind. He'd bring cars here and give people rides in them. The children loved it. I trained the volunteers and explained about confidentiality as part of their induction.

'Lawrence listened respectfully and replied: "I'll do that as long as you don't tell my staff that I'm washing up in the kitchen." He wanted to give the children a fun time and had great empathy and compassion.'

Sister Maureen was grateful to the volunteers.

'They were wonderful people and brought wisdom, experience and goodwill. Their efforts were much appreciated by staff and families. Most volunteers were usually active, retired people. We also had youngsters who wanted to study medicine and needed experience. Two Muslim girls continued to come to help in the kitchen and dining area even during Ramadan when they couldn't eat or drink.

'We also had two retired teachers nicknamed Cagney and Lacey who came every Friday morning to help with cleaning. They arrived early by taxi and could soon be seen with mops, buckets and vacuums. Others had regular weekly mealtime slots. They would help the chef to prepare and serve food and wash up afterwards, leaving the kitchen sparkling clean. A lady called Agnes called in twice a week to look after the flowers and plants.'

Maureen Gordon

To borrow one of her own phrases, Maureen Gordon was a 'bloomin' marvellous' volunteer for Francis House. That was her favourite saying when something went well. Invariably, it always went well if Maureen was involved. Maureen got involved with Francis House in 1996 and got to know Sister Aloysius.

Both shared a determination to get things done and a knack for motivating others for the benefit of the most vulnerable. Maureen trained as a professional cook, skills she used to bake countless delicious dishes and her cakes sold out at hospice open days.

For more than two decades Maureen and husband Dougie held annual all-day garden parties at their home in Chorlton, a tradition continued when they moved to Sale. Visitors were treated to afternoon tea and homemade cakes and pies. Tens of thousands of pounds were raised for Francis House.

Maureen's positivity and can-do attitude touched the lives of everyone she came into contact with. When a task needed doing, Maureen could always be called upon to rally the troops. 'Maureen's Army' as they became known, would consist of 20 to 30 women packing the newsletters into envelopes in the hall at Francis House, or selling Christmas cards at pop-up shops in local libraries.

Maureen was also a familiar face at the Burnage charity shop before it moved to new premises in Withington where she regularly volunteered on Wednesdays. In 2007, she received the Benemerenti papal medal in recognition of her work. Maureen stepped back from volunteering duties two years before she died in February 2022.

Alan Dickinson

Volunteer Alan Dickinson has lost count of his visits to Francis House. His mission each time is returning charity collection tins from shops, pubs and other venues and taking them back again once emptied. Many years ago, the retired insurance agent saw an appeal for bucket collectors in the matchday programme at Manchester United where he was a tour guide.

He recalled: 'The club were involved with Francis House at the time, so I arranged to take part. I've got the "gift of the gab." I enjoy meeting people and thought it sounded like a bit of a laugh.'

It was the start of a long-standing involvement which saw Alan and wife Joyce, from Chadderton, Oldham, take part in collections, bag packs and Christmas fairs. Great grandfather Alan said: 'When you are retired, volunteering gives you something to

Volunteer Alan Dickinson out and about with his collection tin

do and I enjoy it. It's something Joyce and I can do together. I can't abseil up and down buildings, but it's nice to be involved.'

Hospice open days made Alan determined to do as much as he could.

'The hospice is a really happy place; we don't think of it as a sad place. It's fascinating seeing the incredible facilities and everything they do for families is amazing.'

Other Dedicated Volunteers

Preparing and serving meals, answering phone calls and greeting visitors, cleaning and gardening ... no job was too small for the Francis House volunteers! Their efforts front-of-house or behind the scenes saved the charity a small fortune over the years.

Kitchen and reception roles were filled with enthusiasm and distinction by kind-hearted volunteers who deserve a special vote of thanks. Doreen Davies was one of the many long-standing volunteers. Doreen started on reception in 1993 and later assisted with housekeeping and in the kitchen. A presentation was made to the former teacher on her 90th birthday in 2015 to mark more than 30 years of outstanding service.

Grace Cooke retired the same year after more than two decades preparing and serving meals and washing up. Grace was a regular

Long-serving volunteer Grace Cooke seen on her retirement in 2015. Stood are Doreen Davies, Clinical Lead Linda Flowers and Ann Bradley

She said: 'It's been a pleasure to come here every week. You don't work directly with the children because there's a fantastic care team for that. I've even been able to talk to the Polish couples and for them and all the families who come here it's their holiday, a real break.' One of Ron's favourite memories was ringing the hand bell for dinner.

Assisting in the kitchen was the perfect recipe for Sue Altree. Sue, a retired teacher from Cheadle Hulme, spent 15 years at Francis House after joining in 2002 to work in the Saturday tea team. Getting to know people from all walks

fixture on Wednesday lunchtimes, irrespective of weather and personal commitments.

Rita Cartagena's loyal commitment and generous giving of her time did not go unnoticed either. Rita was replaced by Ann Bradley, another stalwart, while Ann Seaston was also a kitchen regular and lived locally. Harold Addie and Lawrence Millett receive honourable mentions elsewhere in this history for their unstinting support.

Other familiar faces inside the kitchen were husband-and-wife Ron and Krystyna Gratton, who spent 19 years volunteering before they stepped down in 2017. The couple were in the crowds when the hospice was opened by Princess Diana in 1991. Krystyna promised that once she retired as an optometrist she would work at Francis House and was true to her word.

Krystyna looked back on her years there with great satisfaction.

Kitchen volunteers Sue Altree and Ron and Krystyna Gratton all gave sterling service

of life was a highlight for Sue who said: 'I had a look around and thought, what a fantastic cause. I felt inspired by what was going on here and wanted to contribute towards it. I've really enjoyed it and the care team have been great. It's a really happy place to work.'

Retired teacher Joan Green spent 24 years as a volunteer. Joan possessed a strong secretarial background and attention to detail which led to her involvement writing the hospice newsletter. Joan also worked on reception and would change from her 'driving' shoes into her 'reception' shoes after entering the building. She joined the hospice in 1992, helping out until she was 90.

Upon her retirement, she said: 'It's been a privilege to be involved with Francis House. I'm now making room for younger people to become involved with the hospice.' Joan died in 2019 at the age of 94. Sister Maureen FMSJ recalled: 'I remember Joan as gentle and caring. She brought a wealth of knowledge and experience to her role, combined with a unique sense of goodwill, support and encouragement. Her contribution to Francis House was invaluable.'

Two of our most loyal kitchen volunteers have been Mike Taylor and Terri Scopelliti. The roles were suspended during Covid but the pair are still an important part of our catering provision and help on Memory Days.

It is impossible to list everyone who has contributed in one way or another. But a sincere thank you to you all. It couldn't have been done without you.

The volunteers without whom Francis House would not be here

CHAPTER 12

BEHIND THE
SCENES

Robin Wood CBE held key positions within two of England's early children's hospices. He was Administrator at Martin House in Wetherby – the third children's hospice to be built – and later took over as Chair of Trustees at Francis House, the fifth in the country. Such unique insight made him an invaluable member of the hospice movement.

From left, Gill Bevin, Robin Wood CBE and David Ireland

Robin Wood CBE

Robin played an integral part in setting up Francis House, guiding organisers through the complicated process of establishing a children's hospice. He attended the charity's launch and, in 1992, crossed the Pennines for a more formal trustee role. He only missed one trustee meeting during 22 years of service. An amazing feat, especially considering he lived in Ilkley, Yorkshire, all of his life.

He stepped down in July 2014 and continued as a trustee until his death the following year. David Ireland, Chief Executive of Francis House, said: 'Robin was an absolute rock as we struggled to launch a charity and build Francis House. He never ceased to be amazed at the speed in which Sister Aloysius accomplished her dream.

'He cared deeply about the children's hospice movement as a whole and was particularly concerned that the support given should be for all the family, not just for the sick child. His experience as chair of a regional health trust in Leeds was invaluable to Francis House and right through his leadership there was a feeling of security. He was the right man for the job and a great support to me, even before I took over as chief executive. He and Lenore Hill, who was Senior Nurse at Martin House, became great friends.'

When Robin retired, chartered accountant Chris Roberts, a trustee since 1992, took over as chair.

Ged Cosgrove

A family connection led to a long-standing involvement with Francis House for accountant Ged Cosgrove. He and his wife adopted three young children from the Catholic Children's Rescue Society in 1988. He stayed in touch with Sister Philomena, a Franciscan Missionary of St Joseph, who had helped make all the necessary childcare arrangements.

When she suggested that Ged's financial expertise would be invaluable for a new children's hospice he readily agreed to offer support. It was the start of a happy relationship with Francis House stretching back more than three decades. Walkden-based Champion, the accountancy firm where Ged is Group Managing Partner, have managed the charity's accounts since day one and act as independent auditors.

Ged attends hospice finance and trustee meetings in an advisory capacity, although he was forced to miss an early meeting. He explained: 'Our son Dominic has spina bifida and I was due to attend either the second, or third meeting around April time in 1990, but had to cancel because we found out about his condition from a scan that same day.

'Every time I go to Francis House, I feel quite lucky that Dominic is fit and well. He drives, lives independently and goes to watch Manchester City. Dominic was born that September and within the first couple of days went to Booth Hall Children's Hospital for an operation on his spinal column. I remember that in a private room a little boy was dying and his dad was sleeping on a mattress on the bed beside him.

Ged Cosgrove meeting the then Duke and Duchess of Cambridge

'That was the state of play before the hospice was in place. Kids just died in hospital and parents had nowhere to go. That little boy might have had brothers and sisters and who was looking after them? That's how it was in 1990 and thankfully things have moved on from then.'

Ged has seen how hard it has been for the charity to make ends meet over the years. He said: 'It was a struggle and initially Salford R.C. Diocese loaned Francis House a sum of £850,000 to help build the hospice. That was paid off over a period of time and was cleared many years ago. I can honestly say we were never down to our last penny. We might have been wondering where the money was coming from for the next year, but the funds started to flow quite quickly.

'I think it's easier to fundraise for a capital cost. When you're actually building something, there's more likelihood people will invest in that. It's harder to fundraise just for ongoing overheads. The hospice was relatively new in the area and it moved forward and the funds came in, together with the loan from the diocese which obviously helped get it off the ground.

'Archbishop Patrick Kelly, the then Bishop of Salford, was a great supporter of Francis House, so that made it easier. Father Thomas Mulheran was involved with Catholic Rescue and sat on the diocesan

The £5m plus raised from the Kirsty Appeal provided a major boost to the charity's finances at the start of the millennium. The driving force behind the campaign, Susie Mathis, was a friend of Ged who introduced her to the hospice. They had raised funds for the Wallness Charity, named after a Salford pub. A small fundraising committee included actress Sue Johnston. Frank 'Foo Foo' Lammar, a well-known Manchester drag queen, was involved, as was former Manchester United captain Bryan Robson who lent his name to a Five Star Scanner Appeal, formerly the Mend A Broken Wing Appeal. Funds from those appeals were used to buy new equipment and refurbish Manchester children's hospital.

Ged said: 'I knew Susie through the charity work our company was involved in. Francis House began their Friend in a Million scheme with the idea everyone gave a pound. It didn't really take off. We were all coming up with these ideas at the hospice and I said: "Why don't we speak to Susie?"

'You can imagine my trepidation introducing Susie Mathis, who was known for her industrial language, to Sister Aloysius. Fortunately, they hit it off and became good friends. There were lots of discussions, with Susie saying we need a figurehead and something to push forward. Some were reluctant to use children, but eventually they came round. Susie very much pushed the Kirsty Appeal which went national with David Beckham involved. She was the mascot for the game with Greece match at Old Trafford when England qualified for the World Cup.

'Kirsty was getting everywhere and was almost a superstar. In terms of direct support, somewhere around £5m to £6m went into the Kirsty fund. The knock-on effect for the charity generally could never be measured really due to the huge profile and awareness which came from it.'

committees which helped with the loan. Sister Aloysius and Sister Austin, together with Father Tom, were all determined that the hospice was going to be built. Bishop Kelly was firmly behind it as well.'

Balancing the books is always a challenge as Ged points out: 'It's getting more difficult and fundraising is getting less and less. Every so often we might get a big legacy, but you can never count on that. We get some funding from the government, but it's not a huge amount.'

Ged is very much part of the fabric at Francis House. 'It's obviously been part of

my life for 30 years and I've seen all the developments. I know my place, so when I go to the hospice and visit the offices, I don't go wandering around. It means I rarely see the children, or the people in it. I look back and think it's a magnificent place to be. It's incredible to see where it came from to what it's doing now, in terms of the hospice, the adolescent wing and then the residential homes at 463 and 92.

'We've been able to do that because we've got the funds and we've been fortunate in that way. There are a lot of charities without the balance sheet we have and that's due to the goodness of people from mainly Greater Manchester, but from far and wide as well as due to the Kirsty Appeal.

'I'm proud of what I've done there to help it along. But it's a great testament to Sister Aloysius, Father Tom and Sister Austin for their belief that it could be done. They all lived to see it be successful and now our Chief Executive David Ireland is carrying it on. It's in good hands. I've seen lots of stories in the press about families and it's been life-changing for them. It's incredible. Years ago, my friend's sister had died and I remember talking to their father. He said: "It's the wrong order. You should never have to bury your child."

'It is probably the worst thing you could possibly do. To think there's support there at that critical time is really what it's all about.'

Martin Lochery

Martin Lochery has been a trustee of Francis House since the start and remembers vividly how he became involved. It was an 'invitation' from hospice founder Sister Aloysius which led to an association lasting more than three decades.

'My first memory was Sister Aloysius, who was a force to be reckoned with,' stated Martin, grinning as he explained the sequence of events which led to his appointment as a trustee in March 1991.

Trustee Martin Lochery

'I was head teacher of St John Vianney, a school on Didsbury Road, Stockport, and my chair of governors was Monsignor Thomas Mulheran, who was also a trustee here. He phoned me up and said: "Martin, Sister would like a word with you."

'I said: "Oh right, okay." I knew who she was and we'd nodded to each other, but I'd never had any significant conversation with her.

'He said: "The easiest thing to do with Sister is just nod and agree."

'I said: "Oh right, thanks Father, I'll remember." So, I met Sister and she told me what Francis House was about and I was suitably impressed, still wondering why I was having this conversation. Then she said: "So you're happy to be a trustee, are you?"

'After a brief pause, I said: "Probably, Sister. I don't really know what that means."

'Before I could say anything else, she replied: "Oh, it's alright. I'll take you through it."

'I don't think I ever formally agreed to be a trustee, but Sister had decided I was going to be one and that was it.'

St John Vianney is a Catholic school for pupils with learning difficulties and complex needs. Martin was therefore used to supporting parents of some 180 pupils receiving education, despite facing severe challenges on a daily basis. Martin was a perfect fit for Francis House.

He said: 'I think that was partly the reason why Sister asked me to become a trustee, because she thought I would have a background knowledge of things. I became involved with meeting some of the families and the difficulties they faced were off the scale in comparison to my school life. This was when the hospice was deciding which families would come here.

'I remember one family at Francis House with two daughters, both of whom were very severely disabled. They could smile and their eyes twinkled, but you wouldn't see much more of a response from them. We heard about the difficulties families faced getting ongoing support. There were lots of individuals who'd helped them at different times, but it was having the security and the knowledge there was somewhere they could trust. People who understood what they were doing and what they could access. That was the thing that hit me most of all. At school, I was used to parents wanting their children to progress and parents sometimes not being quite honest about how their children were performing because they wanted them to do so much better.

'So often you'd get the parents doing the work, for example, and saying the children had done it. That was a fairly regular experience for me. Whereas now you had parents who had children who were capable of very little and yet they were evoking so much love from these families who were having such a tough time.

'It was an amazing experience to feel that you could do a little something to help. That's all it was and being a trustee is a minor thing. I met these families just by chance. It was not formalised at all, but it was such an education for me that it sticks in the mind right from the word go. Fundraising was, of course, an issue. It is ongoing and always has been and will be.

'We have had to ensure the staff have felt supported, acknowledged and understood. I felt that was the more important role of the trustee. The care team were working with the children who might not get better. Francis House was a whole new concept for most of us. Special schools took youngsters with conditions which meant they could also come here.

'We had situations where schools were concerned because respite care was happening during the week when children should have been at school. They were unhappy that the child wasn't at school. In one instance, a school was getting very excited over the fact that their attendance record was falling, partly because of respite care.

'The advantage of me being in the education system was I could explain to them that a child could be marked as present if he or she were at the hospice, with the head's agreement. The head hadn't thought about it and was a bit miffed that no one had ever said it before.'

Martin earned enormous respect for his work in the classroom aiding children with special needs at St John Vianney and was then invited to become Director of Education for Salford R.C. Diocese. Martin was awarded a Papal Knighthood for his services to Catholic education.

He is full of admiration for the staff at Francis House. 'We need trustees and I think we do a good job. But, in reality, we're just a little thing that's at the bottom because of the work that goes on here. The ability of staff to relate to children the way they do and be so open and happy and cheerful with them is mind-blowing.

'Lots of parents have told me coming here is a joy, even though they're visiting with a child who's very, very sick. There's a core element of belief in this place about support for families and all that's required for them, even though we might have some focus on an individual child. Sister Aloysius was undoubtedly a key driver of it, with others. But she was the focal point.

'That has not changed under her successor David Ireland. He has maintained that fundamental belief and attitude throughout. All the trustees also signed up to that and are adamant it won't change. One of the biggest issues is the scientific and medical developments which can extend life expectancy. We had the opening of Francis Lodge for the older ones. So, the whole organisation has had to shift in order to accommodate change.'

Chris Roberts

Running a charity like Francis House is a big responsibility. A dozen trustees are charged with governing and directing how the hospice is managed and run. It was on 28 February 1992 that Chris Roberts attended his first meeting as a trustee. It was a matter of months after the first family was welcomed through the doors.

Much has changed since then at the hospice, with Chris and his colleagues overseeing huge change. He took over as Chair of Trustees in July 2014. Most notably, there has been a period of expansion which has kept Francis House at the forefront of children's palliative care.

Buildings and services have been developed over the years. Progress which has always had the families at the heart of the decision-making process. The board of trustees have played an important strategic role behind the scenes throughout that whole

Chris Roberts, Chair of Trustees from 2014

journey. Making key decisions to shape the future of the hospice, a responsibility which shouldn't be underestimated. Yet Chris is quick to play down the trustee influence. Instead, he prefers to praise staff and volunteers for their selfless work which makes Francis House invaluable to so many families.

Chris said:

'I don't regard myself as having that much of an input at the end of the day. I come, I sign things, I listen. Our Chief Executive David Ireland, or his deputy Rachael Taylor, ring me up and we talk, but my input is strictly limited. Trustees don't get involved on a day-to-day level. That's down to David and his team. We've got some fantastic staff here. They go above and beyond – there's no doubt about it. The trustees aren't on the front-line. It's an executive role and is voluntary. If David wants us to do things we'll help.'

The building of Francis Lodge, a seven-bedroom unit for teenagers and young adults, was one of the biggest decisions made. The Lodge, which cost £3.5m, doubled bedroom capacity when it opened in 2014.

Chris said: 'When we began with our mission for people with short life expectancy, most youngsters were dying before they got into their late teens. Due to medical advances, they're living much longer. I think we have more than 150 teens and young adults we continue to look after. That's something I'm very proud of about Francis House. Some

hospices cut these teenagers off when they reach 18. The service stops. The hospices say: "That's it. You're an adult now."

'We continue to look after them, which is part of our mission statement. Once you're on our books, once we've accepted you, we will look after you and your family. So we built the Lodge to take young adults to give them freedom and independence away from their parents.

'We've also developed our residential side. We have a seven-bedroom unit for permanent residents on Parrswood Road, known as 463. We've also opened a six-bedroom residential unit on Barcicroft Road, in Heaton Moor, for young people with very complex needs. Sister Aloysius had that vision initially to look after people with short life expectancy and it's been followed on by David, who's expanded our services.'

It was through the world of finance that Chris became involved with Francis House. He explained: 'I'm a chartered accountant by profession and our firm were the auditors for Salford R.C. Diocese.

'I met Father Mulheran who said Bishop Kelly, the Bishop of Salford, was looking for volunteers to become trustees. I looked around and the only person in the room was me. The diocese had effectively funded the building of the hospice because Sister Aloysius, in her wisdom, had decided to build Francis House and then seek the money to pay for it.

'The diocese put in quite a substantial loan to fund the building and then keep it going. We've done well financially over the years and the Kirsty Howard Appeal obviously helped enormously. We've also had some very generous donors and continue to

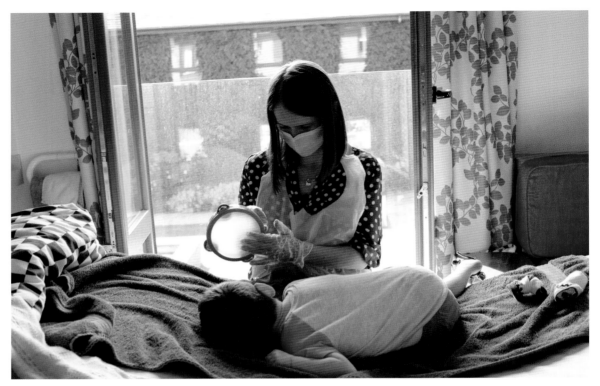

First class care at Francis House

receive legacies we're not expecting. We had one substantial donation from a lady a few months ago. She had not been in contact with us before, but she kindly left us a heck of a lot of money in her will.

'I think the work of Francis House sort of resonates and has done for a long time. We were one of the first children's hospices in the United Kingdom and the first in the north-west. It might sound a bit trite, but children and animals strike a chord with people and the work of the hospice is fantastic.

'I'll be honest with you. A meeting we had in the middle of Covid almost brought me to tears. I was moved by the work staff did to keep this place going when a lot of other children's hospices shut their doors during the pandemic. Staff were going out to

homes wearing full PPE to offer help. It was phenomenal.

'This place is nothing like you'd expect a hospice to be. It's such a happy place. It really is. The young people who come here love it, as do their parents.'

Rachael Taylor

The work undertaken by Rachael Taylor can be as complex as the conditions of the children who use Francis House. The charity's Deputy Chief Executive has an in tray full of different challenges.

'There's something new every day and I never know what I'll be doing next. It's very interesting and rewarding and I enjoy it,' said Rachael, who has been in post since 2012.

She was a trustee for 10 years beforehand, combining that voluntary role with her position as partner in a firm of solicitors. Rachael trained as a family law solicitor and still has a practising certificate, legal expertise which is invaluable helping families at Francis House.

She said: 'I handle all kinds of things. I'm seeing a mum tomorrow who's trying to sort out a benefit claim for her son. He needs total care and is coming up to 18. He needs to apply for benefits and she's in a bit of a tizzy about it and needs some help with the application. He's been coming here since he was tiny. I do all sorts here really to keep the place going.

'A lot of the things we do should be on top of what social services and local authorities should provide, but it doesn't always work like that. We're supposed to provide the extras, but we end up providing basics for people. Families are desperate for respite care which seems to fill such a massive gap in their lives. Francis House is just one of those places. Once you've been here that's it, they've got you for life.'

Rachael works closely with Chief Executive David Ireland to ensure the hospice runs smoothly. Their work covers a wide spectrum, from contracts to care, finance to fundraising and legacies to local authorities. Families are always central to everything that happens.

The small management team led by David and Rachael have control over their own departments but, as senior executives, they take overall responsibility. The paperwork involved in caring for children with such

Rachael Taylor, Solicitor and Deputy Chief Executive at Francis House

serious medical needs is massive. One important document is a Deprivation of Liberty Safeguard (DoLS).

In short, this ensures young adults who cannot consent to their care arrangements due to their mental capacity are protected if those arrangements deprive them of their liberty. Francis House provides respite care for children and young adults aged under 16 and their families. Youngsters stay on the books – if the family wishes – for the rest of their lives.

Regrettably, that means many with severe disabilities are reluctantly turned away, purely because their condition is not life-limiting.

Rachael said: 'There are so many really seriously disabled children living in Greater Manchester, and beyond, with massive needs. They're obviously severely ill and disabled but may have decades of life ahead. Sadly, we can't care for them in our current setting. We have to set some sort of boundaries otherwise we just couldn't cope.

'So our criteria is a life-limiting condition. As you know, a lot of our children live well beyond what they're expected to, partly because of the good care they get from parents and carers, as well as modern science. Treatments that weren't around 10-15 years ago are prolonging lives. We don't have an upper age limit and as people with serious conditions get older, the care they need increases rather than decreases. How can you turn someone away when they need you the most?

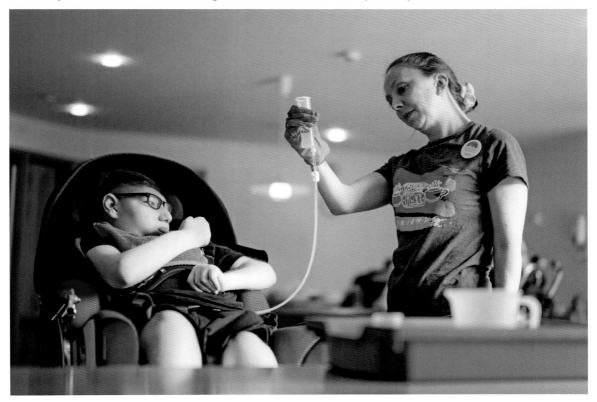

No upper age limit means people like Paul can continue to receive respite care at Francis Lodge

'For someone in that situation in their early 20s, you can't say you're too old. Where do they go? There isn't anywhere for them to go. So, we made a decision a long time ago not to have an upper age limit.'

Two residential units, on Parrswood Road and Barcicroft Road, are exclusively for young adults. These are separate from Francis Lodge, a seven-bedroom facility also for teenagers and young adults, which is the extension to Francis House. Rachael said: 'As a lot of our children grow older, it can become too much for parents. You're not looking after a little one you can pick up and carry around. You're looking after an adult with major nursing care needs. It's a lot for families and they can crack, or parents die, or there are safeguarding issues.

'We see our priority as families and serving their needs. While we're happy to accept grants from the government and from health authorities, the problem is if you start to contract with them, they then expect you to provide a service. That might create a conflict. The service might not then suit the families, but making sure we look after them is our main priority as a charity.

'So, it's difficult if you accept government money. They expect you to do what the government wants you to do. If we don't accept, we retain our autonomy, but it's hard work raising the money. It's a difficult one really. If we could guarantee that what the government wants us to do chimes with what families want, that's what we'd do.'

Francis House relies heavily on fundraising and voluntary donations to meet its costs. Legacies are also a vital source of revenue, though impossible to forecast accurately.

Rachael said: 'We've just had a large sum left to us by someone we had no contact with at all. Things stagnated for a lot of solicitors during Covid, especially with regard to dealing with wills. They're now playing catch up, though a legacy can take over two years to be dealt with. It may sound awful, but sick children are an easy sell in a way. The money we're given is well spent. Every penny we spend we think very carefully about and we haven't got a big administrative team.

'Donations make such a difference to families. You see some of the parents here and for them every day is a battle. They get up and it's hard work. They've got to look after a child who brings an awful lot of joy into their lives, but it's tough for them. With a child with a serious condition, often they can't give the attention to their other children. That's just life for these families, which is why our sibling support service is so important.'

Dean's Kitchen Treats

Chef Dean Jenkins cooked his last meal in 2020 after nearly three decades in Francis House kitchen. Dean joined the hospice in 1991 and led a team of food-loving volunteers serving tasty dishes to youngsters and their families. His kitchen underwent a makeover in 2017, with celebrity chef Simon Rimmer, a keen supporter of the charity, popping in to perform the official opening.

Dean, from Withington, said at the time:

'For the children and families who come here, having a mealtime routine in lives that are often chaotic is extremely important. It takes the pressure off parents as when they come here, they don't have to cook and worry about organising a meal. It really is a great place to work and I couldn't do without our fantastic volunteers.'

All heating and hot water needs are met by Cheadle-based W and G Services, who have been involved with the hospice from the beginning. The late John Woodworth set up the mechanical engineering company, with son David maintaining that long-standing relationship. Similarly, Glen Jones is another loyal tradesman. The owner of Optimum Electrical, he has taken care of electrical work at the hospice throughout most of its history.

Chef Dean Jenkins shares cookery tips with celebrity chef Simon Rimmer, a keen supporter of Francis House

The most impressive job references among staff at Francis House belong arguably to maintenance man, Keith Ireland. He even had the official royal seal of approval. Keith started at the hospice in 2002 before older brother David followed in his footsteps as chief executive three years later.

Keith was an under butler at Buckingham Palace and knew Princess Diana fairly well. He was able to provide references from the Yeoman of the Household and the Butler of the China and Glass Pantry when he applied for the job at the hospice. Keith was well qualified, with an engineering background. His diploma means he can oversee oxygen and medical gases. He also has CORGI training and small electric appliance skills. That versatility keeps costs down for the hospice.

The Face of Francis House

When young people in wheelchairs arrived at Francis House they were greeted by a warm welcoming smile from Carmel Holland. She used a wheelchair, a reassuring sign for families who knew immediately that here was a place which fully understood the needs of youngsters who needed special help.

Carmel was a receptionist from the day the hospice opened, having occupied the same role with the Catholic Children's Rescue Society. Her familiar face welcomed visitors for 29 years until she left in March 2020. It was Covid which eventually brought her stay to an end. Her condition meant she had to be furloughed and she received voluntary redundancy.

Staff take time out from their duties for a team photograph

Another long-serving member of staff was Margaret Stelmaszek, who was secretary from July 1992 and later became a receptionist and PA to the fundraising manager. Margaret left once the pandemic arrived.

Edith Nercessian was PA to Sister Aloysius from March 1992 until July 2005. Edith was employed in the fundraising office initially and later helped on reception when she reduced her working hours.

Ann Kirwin was another key member of the team for many years, having been PA to the CEO and all three Directors of Care. Ann joined Francis House in June 2004 and left as a result of Covid in August 2021. Karen Smail is a more recent recruit. She started as secretary in 2018 and became PA in 2021. After various attempts to manage the gardens, the millennium saw the arrival of Carol Hewitt who has been caring for the hospice grounds ever since.

The Trustees and Council of Management

The 12 trustees who decide how Francis House is run come from a variety of professional and cultural backgrounds. A total of 29 trustees have served over the years, meeting quarterly with a general meeting held annually.

Monsignor Thomas Mulheran with the Right Reverend Terence John Brain, a trustee for 23 years and Bishop of Salford R.C. Diocese for 17 years

These boots were made for walking ... trustee Judith Amosi-Khodadad is one of the hospice trekkers

The fact that such a relatively small number have served a hospice which has been open for 32 years illustrates the longevity and loyalty of those who voluntarily lead the charity. It is a diverse list, representing different faiths and skills, including legal, financial, educational and medical backgrounds.

Several long-serving trustees are featured elsewhere in this book. Deserving also of a mention is The Right Reverend Terence John Brain, who served as a trustee from 1997 to 2020. He was Bishop of Salford R.C. Diocese from 1997 until 2014 and is now retired.

Dr Hugh Fay was a member between 1990 and 2004, while Rev. Bernard Wilson served as a trustee for 17 years until 2019. Mrs Sheena Nolan was on the management group from 1998 until 2013. Current trustees Dr Sue Kirk and Dr Susan O'Halloran have been members since 2009 and 2011 respectively.

Many get involved in other ways as well to support the hospice. For instance, teacher Judith Amosi-Khodadad has joined hospice fundraising treks. Her first adventure was to the ancient site of Petra in 2013, the year she became a trustee.

Judith, who also volunteered on reception, said:

'I got involved after I dropped off clothes and toys for the charity shop. Francis House is an incredible place and it's lovely to see the smiling faces of the children.'

CHAPTER 13

DOCTORS

In the history of Francis House no one could have had a more fitting name than Dr Stanley Goodman. The charity's first Medical Director was a good man and a good doctor. That he lived up to his name is beyond question. The offer of his services from the very start was also a stroke of good luck for Francis House.

Dr Goodman had been medical advisor to Manchester Adoption Society for 25 years, a longevity of service towards the care of children requiring support that made him ideally suited to Francis House. The GP practice where he was lead doctor was based in nearby Ladybarn, serving the residents of Burnage, Withington and Fallowfield.

The fledgling Francis House was willingly added to the practice portfolio, with Dr Goodman emphasising the need to support parents of children with life-limiting illnesses. Such was his passion and dedication for his hospice role that he promised to remember every single case.

He honoured this pledge after immediately warming to the charity, saying: 'You only have to go through the door and realise it's a place full of friends.' Over time it became clear that as the demands of Francis House were increasing, so too were the everyday challenges presented by a growing caseload of patients at Dr Goodman's practice.

Ladybarn therefore withdrew from the arrangement rather reluctantly. In the summer of 1995, a new more sustainable system of GP support was implemented, with GPs drawn from different practices in the area sharing medical responsibility. Francis House remained close to Dr Goodman's heart until his death in December 1997.

Part of his legacy was to inspire the next generation of GPs who provided medical cover 24 hours a day, seven days a week. Among them Dr David Dawson and Dr Emma Leon, each clocking up more than a quarter of a century of service at Francis House. A GP visits the hospice every day to meet children and families and tend to any medical needs.

Dr Dawson retired in March 2022, though the family name was still proudly associated with Francis House. Two years earlier, daughter Kirsty followed in her father's footsteps by becoming a qualified GP and she joined the medical team.

Father David said upon his retirement: 'When the opportunity came to work at Francis House it was my ideal job. When I first came in 1995, I thought, wow this is totally above and beyond what could be provided on the NHS. I was overawed by what Francis House was offering the children in terms of the facilities, multi-sensory rooms, tactile experiences and wonderful toys.

'In the early days while on call, I was able to take my own children with me and they would have their lunch at Francis House. My daughter Kirsty went from the age of four or five and she is now a doctor herself there and I can retire now because of that continuity.

'It has been enjoyable looking after the children. People think a hospice is a sad place and how could I do it, but it's not sad. We often have a laugh. Yes, children do die but you have to accept that. Some of the most important and memorable times for me were spent with the bereaved siblings during the Shining Stars sessions, just sitting and talking and spending time with the brothers and sisters. I've met so many families and parents over the years and I was always pleased to see them. The children knew your name and would chat to you. I'm proud to have been part of the team and enjoyed the holistic approach to care.'

Two other GP stalwarts also stepped down shortly before David. Dr Andy Wright retired in 2021 after 13 years at the charity, while

Dr Emma Leon who co-ordinates the Francis House GPs

the previous year saw the departure of Dr John Swarbrick after 16 years in post. The six doctors comprising the Francis House team are drawn from practices in Heaton Moor, Gatley and Poynton. Their co-ordinator is the vastly experienced Dr Emma Leon, a locum and GP appraiser.

Dr Leon said: 'Most of our time is spent advising on acute problems which may or may not be related to the child's underlying condition. We will also, of course, be available for end-of-life care to help support the young person and their family physically and psychologically when needed.

'All the doctors are GPs with a special interest in paediatric palliative care. We all work closely with each other, plus children's hospital teams including consultants, community nurses and social workers, to give the child the best possible care at any given time. Francis House has been a huge part of my working life. I saw an advert for a job here in my first year as a GP in Heald Green.

I remember that day clearly. A piece of A4 paper came into my in tray and it appealed to me hugely.

'I lived in Didsbury at the time and knew of the hospice. It's been a real privilege to be involved in such a special place over such a long time. I'm here at least once a week and handle referrals, liaise with hospital consultants and families and discharges to GPs when any change has taken place here. I also look after the rotas and any educational and training needs for other GPs. We have a doctor who comes in here every day and who is on call for 24 hours.

'Children are in here for respite care for typically maybe three or four days, sometimes a bit longer. Often there's a child coming in on your day on rota and you gradually get to know them and how they are and whether they're 'well' in themselves. Children who come here are, by the nature of the place, unwell with an underlying chronic illness and there may be an acute illness that might happen on top of that.

'They're all vulnerable to pain, infection, skin issues, breathing and seizures, so there's a lot that can happen when children are here. But just like any child, if they're acutely unwell and they need emergency care they go to hospital. Some children here will have 'do not resuscitate' forms. They tend to be the much more seriously unwell children, but the vast majority will be for full resuscitation and will go to hospital with a 999 call.

'A lot of the GP work, though, can be treating the same ailments as for any child. It can still be chest infections, coughs, urinary tract infections and skin stuff and other normal symptoms. Then it becomes more specialised during end-of-life care or when symptom control is more in-depth.

'Francis House is a warm, friendly, lovely and homely sort of place. It doesn't have a sad vibe. Instead, it has an uplifting feel to it. That's how it is most of the time, but plainly there are times when it's sad. Deaths happen here, but the upside is that if you manage a death well and if it goes well for a child and their family then you've actually done a really good job.

'Then it becomes satisfying, as well as sad. Obviously, you're going through that incredibly intimate period of time with a family and you wouldn't be human if you didn't feel the emotion in it. Yes, we're one step removed, but you still feel the sadness. We have a relatively new team of young doctors who're less experienced in a place like this and our main aim is to work really well together and support each other.

'We had a new child in yesterday for end-of-life care and the doctor on call then was leading that child's care. We had a Zoom call together this morning as a group to plan ahead to obviously provide optimal care. As much as anything it is important to give doctors support so they don't feel like they're on their own dealing with what can be quite a scary, challenging situation.'

●●●

Medical advances mean that extremely sick children are living longer than before. But as science progresses, so too does the complexity of treatment a youngster receives for a specific condition. Doctors at Francis House are at the

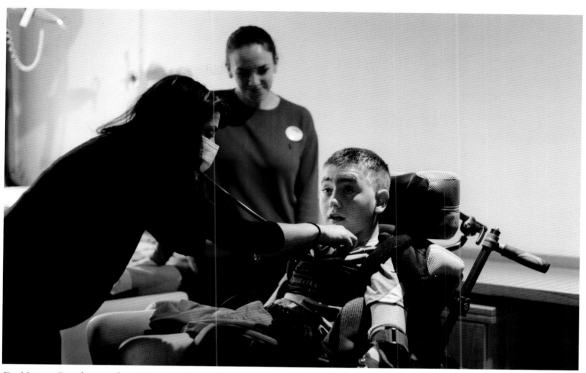

Dr Nutan Patel one of six Francis House doctors who provide on-call cover seven days a week and visit the hospice every day

forefront of that specialist palliative care for some illnesses which are even undiagnosed.

Dr Emma Leon said:

'As medicine has moved on, so the complexity of what we're able to do to help the children has evolved. We can look after children with more severe illness for a longer period of time, whether through ventilation, different medication procedures, or through use of oxygen. We're doing an awful lot more, so young people are living a lot longer. But that can mean more issues develop which need to be addressed and the medicine is therefore much more complex.'

It is a far cry from when Dr Leon was embarking on a medical career. She said: 'When I started out, specialist paediatric palliative care was very much in its infancy. It was a merge of adult palliative care and paediatrics, but not a speciality in its own right. Then, as children with life-limiting illnesses were living longer, there became a need for a stand-alone speciality, so hospital training courses and consultancy paediatric palliative care were developed.

'From a general practice perspective, statistically most GPs would come across one child death in their whole career. So, fortunately, it's a very rare occurrence in society and this is therefore a very unusual place for a GP to work because you wouldn't normally have the experience of coming across a child dying, whether it was a child born with a life-limiting condition, or a child who was essentially well and then developed a disease that made them die.

'It's still rare for a general GP to come across that sort of problem and look after the child and, of course, their family so we very much learned on the job. Over the last 15 years or so there have been specialist training schemes and education days and much more around to actually learn from, but a lot of it is learning from each other and developing the experience as you go along. Each case is unique because children are inherently strong, so you don't really know how they're going to respond to a condition they have. Plainly, each family is unique and everyone works in a different way as a family.

'We come across challenges all the time, both from a physical perspective in terms of the symptom control, but also psychological and social aspects. Quite a number of cases are undiagnosed. Children have been to genetic and neurology clinics, but there's an awful lot we still don't know. But then you work with symptoms and you just follow the child.'

●●●

Every death at Francis House is reviewed by the clinicians and care team. Dr Emma Leon said: 'Every death is used as part of a learning process – is there anything we can do better next time? Is there anything we can take away? Often there is. It could be through the use of a different drug, or different dose, or any communication changes.

'Every child has their own GP and their own team of consultants, but here they're our responsibility. Very often they are far from home, so if they need to see a doctor while here, they'll see us. We have quarterly GP and heads of care meetings at which we review each death and children whose acute and complex needs need to be discussed.

'We also sort out referrals to ascertain if a child is suitable to come to Francis House and gather their medical histories, including prognosis. What we won't do here ever is say, "You're too old to come any more; you're going to have to go somewhere else for your respite care."'

'Predominantly that's because there's nowhere really similar that you could say it's time for you to be going to that particular place. So, we have to get referrals right as best we can at that stage. They may be babies or any age up to 16. We've only got a handful of people in their 30s at Francis House and that's stretching it. Really, once you're getting into your mid-teens, unless you've got a relatively short prognosis, it's not appropriate for you to be coming to Francis House.

'Having said that, the young men with Duchenne muscular dystrophy come and we know they're unlikely to live into their 30s, but we feel that they definitely get an improved quality of life from coming here through their teens and 20s. If their prognosis was such that they didn't have a life expectancy below say their mid 20s, because then there's nowhere else for them to go. There's a real lack of respite care facilities for young or middle-aged adults. We've got old-age nursing homes with maybe day care type facilities, but there's nothing like this for people in their 20s or 30s.'

CHAPTER 14

COVID

The Covid-19 outbreak caused worldwide panic in spring 2020. For Francis House the pandemic presented a unique and difficult challenge. Social distancing, face masks, lockdowns and hand gels became part of everyday life for us all.

But for children with underlying health conditions, the coronavirus disease presented a grave danger. They were among vulnerable groups at greatest risk from the spread of the terrible virus which swept the globe. Francis House stayed open for children requiring end-of-life care who had Covid, whose families might have Covid or for emergency situations.

Regrettably, regular respite care had to be cancelled. Director of Care Gill Bevin had reduced her working hours to three days a week by March 2020, in preparation for her retirement later that year. She was being shadowed by Sharon Doodson, who had been appointed as her replacement in December 2019.

Once Covid arrived, it was action stations as far as the charity was concerned. The emergency meant Gill returned to full-time as they both coordinated a response to safeguard children, families and staff and she was finally able to retire in November 2020.

Sharon recalled: 'As you can imagine, Covid was a nightmare and everything was turned upside down once Covid hit. Every rule went out of the window as regards what you'd normally do. No one knew what we were supposed to be doing and how we were supposed to manage it, so we were trying to learn as we went along.

'Even though we cancelled regular respite, we still took families in with Covid. Any parents who had Covid we'd take care of their child for them, because they were too frightened to be around their child. At the very beginning no one knew what it was, or what it was going to be. We had to scrape personal protective equipment (PPE) from everywhere we could because we weren't sent it initially.

'We bought gowns and masks from all over the place and after eight months eventually secured a supply through the NHS hub. We set up two Covid suites specifically for young people with Covid who had aerosol generating procedures. Other young people were isolated in bedrooms for the whole of their stay. The whole hospice was kept safe.'

Staff rallied round during the hospice's greatest hour of need. Sharon said: 'None of the staff ran away from it. They've all got families at home, but there wasn't one person who didn't want to help look after the people coming in. This was at a time when we had no idea whether we could catch the disease or die from it. We just didn't know at that point. It was challenging and scary.

'We had a 13-year-old boy who came for end-of-life during Covid at a time when hospitals were only allowing one person in at a time to be with their family member, even at end-of-life. So, we closed off a whole area of the hospice so the family could come and be with their son at end-of-life. That was in the April when Covid was rife.

'Because of the size of the hospice we were able to separate them completely so they didn't mix with anyone and staff wore PPE. The family were safe in their own bubble and could be together for that child who had a life-limiting condition but didn't have Covid. We managed the funeral for them here as well so that he could have a proper send-off. There were limits on numbers attending a funeral, so we risk-assessed it. It was strategically managed so a member of staff was responsible for each household. They were separated and kept at a distance so that they didn't mix.

'We were able to do the funeral in the chapel with each family hub a safe distance from each other. The staff would direct them out in a safe way so they couldn't spread Covid.

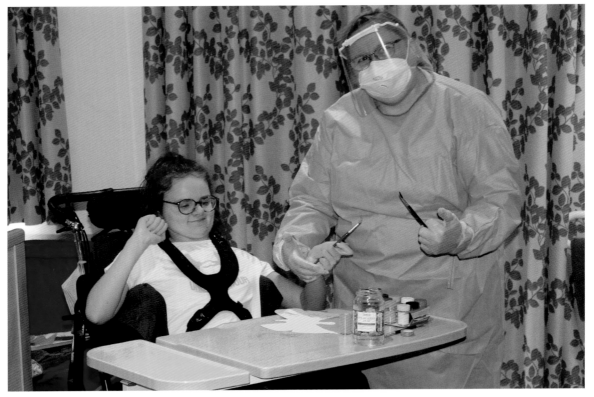

Activities continued during Covid as carer Dawn Geddes takes every precaution with Isabel

Covid did not remove the smile from Thabani's face

it to Francis House. I was really confident with the care team. A lot of training is provided for the staff who work here. Although Covid was a big unknown, I knew about "barrier" nursing which is infection control. I'd been used to dealing with serious infections during my nursing career. So, I knew how to care for people with infections that were potentially life-threatening to me and others should I pass it on. I knew we had to apply the same theory here.

'We also had three young people from our residential unit who had Covid and were put into separate rooms. The gowns were horrible. They were sticky and sweaty, but it was all we could get at the time. Staff wore them all day and did activities such as art therapy to keep the youngsters occupied. Not one person complained about it – they were fantastic.'

For Gill Bevin, the ever-changing government advice was a challenge to say the least. She said: 'I'd been in post 10 years and was confident in my job, but I felt like I was rewriting the rule book for policies and procedures. No one worries so much about Covid now, but at that time there were hundreds dying each day in the country. I was rewriting procedures every night. The next day everything I'd read up on the previous night was thrown out of the door as advice had changed. Then it changed again the day after that.

'The government didn't tell us what to do. They gave us guidance and we had to apply

'I was very confident the care team could handle infection control. My biggest fear and worry in March 2020 was actually the staff. I was confident the children would be looked after correctly and we wouldn't pass it from one child to another. Initially, though, I was bothered about the staff getting it from the child and taking it home.'

The hospice looks back with great pride at how it kept the service running. Doctors, supervisors, pharmacists, consultants and support staff all showed amazing resilience to care for sick young people during this difficult time.

CHAPTER 15

INTERNATIONAL WORK

The name of Francis House is well known across the globe with its reputation for helping sick children. The charity has helped several countries establish hospice facilities. Bosnia, Belarus, Japan, Australia, Canada, USA, Czech Republic and Latvia have all received assistance at one time or another, including during times of crisis.

For instance, babies born with deformities as a result of the Chernobyl nuclear disaster received help from Francis House. Kathy Cooper from the charity's home care team visited Belarus in the early 2000s to educate nurses on pain relief for the children of children who had been affected by radiation. The babies with life-limiting conditions were born to mothers who were children themselves at the time of the nuclear accident in neighbouring Ukraine in 1986.

Francis House also supplied equipment, which was out of date in the UK, but which was gratefully accepted by paediatric specialists in Belarus. The Chernobyl project was not the only disaster zone to benefit from the charity's international efforts.

Francis House went to Bosnia Herzegovina to help set up a seven-bed hospice in Tuzla, a mining town ravaged by a civil war after the break-up of Yugoslavia. Chief Executive David Ireland and Head of Care Margaret Hickie visited the mountainous region in 2006, more than a decade after the bitter fighting ended.

Part of a hospital built originally for patients with mining-related breathing difficulties was converted into a hospice with vital input from Francis House. Its involvement came about due to the reputation as a centre of excellence for respite childcare. Francis House helped with design, clinical care and training.

David and Margaret delivered lectures about children's hospice work for medical experts from Bosnia, Romania and Montenegro, plus neighbouring countries. To reach Tuzla, they endured an arduous six-hour car journey from the capital Sarajevo which had been under siege for four years during the war.

David said:

'Sarajevo was still war-torn and there were graves on the central reservation of the streets because they had run out of places to bury people. It was quite a frightening experience. We were put into a car and dropped in the middle of nowhere on our way to Tuzla. No one spoke English and when we eventually reached our destination, we supplied the information to build a new hospice.'

Dr Emma Leon, along with Margaret and care team colleague Gill Bevin, went to Bosnia in 2008 to train staff. Nurses and doctors from the Tuzla facility have also visited Francis House to learn about paediatric palliative care. A translator used by the hospice, who had escaped from the horrors of Sarajevo by crawling through a sewer with her child, eventually studied nursing in Wales.

A Japanese delegation visit Francis House. From left, Gill Bevin, Director of Care Francis House; Rie Yamaji, Hospital Play Specialist, Osaka City General Hospital; Hisato Tagawa, Representative Director of Yokohama Children's Hospice Project; Professor Takatora Sato, Asahikawa University, Representative Director of Hokkaido Children's Hospice Project; David Ireland, Chief Executive Francis House; Yuko Moue, Representative Director of Paediatric Brain Tumour Association and Hitoshi Hoshino, Member of Yokohama Children's Hospice Project.

The Ocean and Sky Children's Hospice in Yokohama

Francis House has never incurred costs during its work abroad. All funding has come from overseas non-government organisations keen to utilise its charitable expertise. A centre in Yokohama which opened in November 2021 was inspired by Francis House.

The Ocean and Sky Children's Hospice is modelled on the Didsbury concept by embracing families holistically and fulfilling a child's life rather than merely waiting for the end to come. Incredibly, the Yokohama facility is only the second children's hospice in Japan. The first, in Osaka, opened in 2012. There are an estimated 20,000 children in Japan with life-threatening conditions, with most either in hospital or at home. Other cities are working hard to establish a children's hospice facility, envious of the progress made by Francis House. Representatives from Yokohama visited Manchester on a fact-finding mission in 2018.

The Ocean and Sky delegation was led by Hisato Tagawa who wanted to build a hospice because of an acute lack of respite care available for his young daughter, Haruka. She had died of a brain tumour. It was the start of a strong relationship between Francis House and Ocean and Sky, a name derived from its port location at the mouth of Tokyo Bay.

David Ireland used his architectural expertise to advise on the design of the building working with Japanese architect Isao Tsushima who had to cope with the challenges of earthquakes and the threat of tsunami. David said: "The hospice ground floor is a storage area because of its tsunami problem, with the children on the floor above, so if there's a flood they won't be affected.

'We helped them in several ways. The Yokohama project is designed by one of Japan's leading architects, but for us it was more about planning and how things fit together. The Yokohama team also visited us for training. It was going to be delayed due to a lack of builders before the Olympics, but when the venues weren't needed for spectators due to Covid the hospice was finally completed and opened initially as a day care centre.

'Gill and I returned to Yokohama in February 2020 just as the Covid outbreak struck. An American cruise ship was quarantined in the harbour and we did wonder briefly if we'd get home. We had to go into quarantine on our return. We'd been speakers at a gathering of the International

Expertise from Francis House was used to help plan a hospice in Yokohama

Children's Palliative Care Network, a forum attracting experts from all branches of medicine. The year before we had delivered the keynote speech at the same conference.'

Another keen supporter of the Yokohama project was translator Sachie Iiyama who went to school in England. She visited Francis House with Mr Tagawa and Professor Tora Sato. The Professor had volunteered at Francis House in the early days while studying at Manchester University. He came because he was planning a hospice in Hokkaido, the northernmost Japanese island, where there is now a small two-bed facility.

The Francis House influence abroad does not end there. In December 2022, consultants visited from the Czech Republic to explore ways of setting up a children's hospice in Prague. Their trip followed initial visits by the Klicek Foundation, which is based in the capital.

Francis House has also welcomed organisations from Australia, Canada, USA and Latvia over the years to offer advice on paediatric palliative care.

David said:

'Part of me approaches this as a religious minister who just wants to help as many people as possible through our international work. We want to be seen as a charity that, by using non-government organisation funds without any cost to Francis House, is able to do a lot of good in the world.'

CHAPTER 16

CONCLUSION

A worthwhile error… that was how Sister Aloysius summed up building Francis House. The error was deciding to go ahead with the project back in 1990 with hardly any money. Sister made the reference in a BBC television programme about Francis House. She was right.

It might be considerd a mistake to take such a major risk. But she was also correct in saying that it was a gamble worth taking.

The fact that more than 1,500 families have been helped, in some form or another, since the charity started keeping records is all

The welcoming front entrance to Francis House

Francis House provides a safe, spacious environment

the evidence needed to show it was well worthwhile.

Revd David Ireland and Sister Maureen FMSJ were both involved from the start, David as architect, trustee, minister and chief executive.

He said: 'It was a worthwhile error, that's the right phrase. Sister Aloysius had signed the contract without any knowledge of where the money was coming from. It all happened very quickly because the need was great.

'When we opened there was nothing else in this area north of Birmingham, west of the Pennines, nor in Ireland or Scotland. It was a roller-coaster ride because there was no money. Eventually the north-west got behind us and we managed to achieve stability. Sister Aloysius signed the contract

with hardly any money in the bank. It was a nerve-wracking time.

'Father Tom was Secretary to the Catholic Children's Rescue Society and eventually the Finance Secretary for Salford R.C. Diocese. He said: "Just let her get on with it. They rarely send nuns to prison and if they do, she needs a sabbatical."

'Unbeknown to me, he had already brokered a £750,000 loan from the diocese, but he couldn't say that at the time. Repaying the loan, which eventually reached £850,000, was not on Sister Aloysius' mind either. Sister didn't pay anything back. She thought the loan should just disappear into the ether and be forgotten about. We had this £1.4m debt hanging over us when I took over as Chief Executive in 2005. It was interest free but increased in line with the retail price index so it had gone up.

'We wanted the hospice to move on but couldn't really expand with this loan there. The economy was fairly buoyant and fundraising was going well, so I started paying off the loan as quickly as we could. I wanted to clear it. The site is still owned by the Rescue Society, which is now Caritas, so they are our landlords and we pay rent to them.'

Francis House is in safe hands. Through shrewd management, it is financially stable though there is always the need to keep fundraising. Looking to the future, perhaps the biggest concern is how to help more families. Youngsters with life-limiting illnesses are living longer thanks to medical interventions and improved care methods.

The latest figures show 573 families on the books. That has more than quadrupled in

Room with a view... (above) a bedroom in Francis Lodge (below) the red room in Francis House

the last two decades. There were 138 families cared for in 2005. Demand for those precious services provided by Francis House will only increase. That means more space, and staff, will be required at some point ideally.

It was the Franciscan Missionaries of St Joseph – the so-called Rescue Sisters – who gave up their convent to make way for Francis House in 1990. Sister Maureen FMSJ is part of that order. Ever since, she has worked tirelessly to care for the children and young adults who effectively took over her own home. A sacrifice she never regretted.

Sister Maureen said: 'I have wonderful memories of amazing kids and families. We are privileged because they've placed their trust in us. You see the love of a parent for a child and the protection given to them, regardless of religion. We pray for the children and families. Who knows what prayer is doing? For all Sisters, whatever job you're doing, you take that as God's work. God's asking you to do that.'

For everyone involved at Francis House over the years there has been lots of joy and happiness. Smiles and laughter. Care and compassion. Love and affection. Sweat and toil too. The inevitable tears of sadness as well. Thanks for the memories.

The story continues...

Senior hospice care team at Francis House

FRANCIS HOUSE
CHILDREN'S HOSPICE

ACKNOWLEDGEMENTS

Pauline Armitage MBE, Claire Armstrong, Judy Bailey, Gill Bevin,
Andrew Clarke, Ged Cosgrove, Sharon Doodson,
Mary and Alan Gillatt, Jackie Graham, Natalie Hands,
Margaret Hickie, Revd David Ireland, Sister Joan FMSJ,
Dr Emma Leon, Martin Lochery, Esther Lowery,
Sister Maureen FMSJ, Rachel Nasiri, Sister Philomena FMSJ,
Kate Puć, Chris Roberts, Karen Smail, Sir Warren Smith KCVO
KStJ JP, Rachael Taylor, Kyle Wells, David Woodrow

Special thanks to Karen Flower,
Francis House Public Relations & Press Officer

DONATIONS

Francis House Children's Hospice is a charitable organisation and relies on donations.

If you feel that you could donate, please send a cheque made payable to **'Francis House Family Trust' to Francis House Children's Hospice, 390 Parrswood Road, Didsbury, Manchester M20 5NA.**

Please let us know the reason for your donation and include your full name, address, postcode and contact email address so that we can write and thank you if you wish.

If you are a UK taxpayer your donation will be worth 25 per cent more. Gift Aid is reclaimed by the charity from the tax you pay for the current tax year. Your address is needed as a current UK taxpayer.

To make a donation over the phone using a credit/debit card, contact our fundraising office on **0161 434 2200.**

Please visit our website **www.francishouse.org.uk** to donate online or set up a regular gift.

We would like to keep you up to date with news of Francis House, but in order to do that you would need to confirm that you are happy for us to contact you by email.

You can change how we communicate with you at any time. Please contact **fundraising@francishouse.org.uk** or call **0161 443 2200**. To understand how Francis House looks after your data, please see our privacy policy at **www.francishouse.org.uk/privacy-policy**

SCAN TO DONATE

We thank you for your support.